Mr. Madison's War

1812: The Second War for Independence

Mr. Madison's War

1812:
THE SECOND WAR FOR INDEPENDENCE

by

Noel B. Gerson

Maps by Barry Martin

JULIAN MESSNER
NEW YORK

Published by Julian Messner
Division of Pocket Books, Inc.
8 West 40 Street, New York 10018

© Copyright 1966 by Noel B. Gerson

Printed in the United States of America

Library of Congress Catalog Card No.: 66-14001

For
MICHELE

Mr. Madison's War

1812: The Second War for Independence

Just three decades after the American colonies won the Revolutionary War, the young nation became embroiled in a new war with England. The significance of this war is often overshadowed by the importance of the one that preceded it—but the War of 1812 was the first genuine test of whether Americans were willing and able to sustain the most democratic government man had yet conceived. How a young country put an end to sectional differences when her trade by sea was threatened, and functioned as a nation, indivisible, for the first time, is absorbing reading.

Books by Noel B. Gerson

MR. MADISON'S WAR:
1812: The Second War for Independence

ROCK OF FREEDOM:
The Story of the Plymouth Colony

CHAPTER ONE

"If we don't win a battle soon, the whole world is going to think Americans don't know how to defend their country or their honor. What a war!" Young Captain David Shoemaker of the Maryland militia leaned on the parapet of chest-high earthworks, sighed, and rubbed the stubble on his chin. "We've taken beating after beating!"

Lieutenant Harry Greene, his immediate subordinate, replied with a tired yawn. The sun was a huge, glowing orange ball on the horizon to the east, and soon their company would be relieved of sentry duty after standing watch all night. It would be too hot to sleep, of course. August was always impossibly warm and humid on Chesapeake Bay, and the whole summer of 1814 had been uncomfortable.

Harry couldn't help wishing he were stationed somewhere other than this quiet spot on the western shore of the Bay, even if it meant retreats and forced marches to the rear. For two long, dreary years Americans had been losing battle after battle to the British. But the men who had fought in those engagements were luckier, Harry thought, than the commanders of half-trained militiamen who never saw anything more menacing than a herd of cows grazing in a pasture. Action—any kind of action—was preferable to doing nothing.

"What bothers me," Shoemaker went on, "is that the Redcoats can't be that good. When I was a boy I heard my

father and my uncle talk about the way we whipped them
during the Revolution. Today's Lobsterbacks can't be that
much better than the older generation."

Harry grinned. "Maybe they aren't. Maybe we're worse.
Look at our record—two solid years of defeats. Then look
at old General Winder."

"I'd rather not." No military man felt any respect for
W. H. Winder, the brigadier general charged with the defense of Washington City, the nation's new and growing
capital. He was a politician, not a soldier, and every officer
in his command knew it. "Not that I can blame him, really,"
Shoemaker added. "The men who fought under Washington are either dead or too old to go into the field again, and
our new commanders haven't had any experience. It's no
wonder the Redcoats keep whipping us. We're a country of
amateur soldiers who thought we'd never have to fight another war. The British knew it, and they've taken advantage
of us by sending an army of professional troops to lick the
daylights out of us."

Harry's smile faded. "What do you think will happen,
Dave?"

Shoemaker shrugged, but his face was grim. "I keep
praying for a miracle that doesn't occur. At least there's one
ray of hope. In the Revolution at one time or another the
Lobsterbacks occupied Philadelphia and New York and
Boston. In this war our major cities have been spared—so
far."

Suddenly Harry gasped and pointed with a trembling
finger toward a long line of ships heading up the Patuxent,
a calm river that meandered through the Maryland flatlands
and emptied into Chesapeake Bay, east of Washington City.

The British Union Jack flew proudly from the mastheads
of huge ships-of-the-line, the largest and most powerful war
vessels ever to sail the seven seas. Each carried a minimum
of seventy-four great cannon, and all were primed and ready

for action, their muzzles protruding from open gun-ports. Shepherding the giants were sleek frigates, the greyhounds of the sea, each mounting twenty to forty great cannon.

There were many smaller vessels in the great fleet, too. Trim sloops of war, the fastest and most graceful ships afloat, darted in and out of the awe-inspiring line, holding cumbersome troop transports in place like collie dogs nipping at the heels of cattle. There were ugly, squat ketches whose bombs could destroy American harbors, docks, and warehouses, as well as all merchant ships unable to escape their wrath. And bringing up the rear were several converted brigs, former civilian ships whose small guns were capable of driving away similarly armed American privateers that might, in their desperation, launch suicide attacks on the great armada.

"Invasion!" Harry exclaimed.

"I spoke too soon. Sure as shooting, they're going to attack Washington City." Shoemaker quickly pulled himself together. "Lieutenant Greene, sound the alarm! Alert the regiment!"

"Yes, sir!"

A few moments later bugles sounded and drums rolled. Sleepy American militiamen came out of their tents, rubbed their eyes in wonder when they saw the great armada, and immediately went to work under the direction of their officers.

Only one defense was possible, and as the leaders of the small American force knew, it was inadequate. But they had no choice. Their only, slim hope of beating back an attack was to build higher, stronger earthworks. The soldiers dug frantically into the soft, moist Maryland earth and piled fresh dirt on their above-the-ground trenches.

The younger men glanced at each other uneasily. Most of them had been born in the thirty-one years since the United States had won her independence and had never seen such a tremendous display of naval power. Even the few officers and sergeants who remembered Admiral Lord Howe's fleet from the days of the Revolution were stunned by the enemy's demonstration of overwhelming strength.

"Higher, boys!" Shoemaker shouted as he moved up and down his company's line, sword in hand. "Second platoon, swing your picks harder! Shovel faster!"

Harry was busy, too, urging the men to show greater speed and trying, at the same time, to keep up their spirits. "Don't stand there gaping at those floating piles of lumber. Get ready to give them a warm welcome!"

In spite of the officers' exhortations, however, the work went slowly. The militiamen weren't lacking in personal courage, yet they were numbed by fear. Some were boys still in their late teens, others were in their early twenties, and all, at best, were part-time soldiers who had left farms and foundries and fishing boats to help their country in a time of urgent need. None had ever faced an enemy or fired a musket in earnest, and the prospect that awaited them was terrifying.

A major who was second-in-command of the regiment helped to ease the tension momentarily. "See the name of that first monster out there, lads?" he shouted in a deep, booming voice. "She's the *Invincible*. Do you know why they call her that? Because our *Constitution* hasn't caught up with her yet. Invincible, is she? Ha! When the *Constitution* is finished with her, her name will be mud!"

A ripple of laughter greeted the sally, and for a short time the companies labored with greater vigor, throwing their wall of earth still higher. As all of them knew, their comrades in the infant United States Navy had wrought real miracles since the beginning of the war and had proved that American ships and American seamen were superior to the enemy. In fact, the Navy's consistently heroic performance had been the one bright spot in an otherwise dismal two-year war record. It had proved again and again that the British, in spite of their superiority in arms, their fine training, and their magnificent discipline, were only human.

The *Invincible* and the two men-of-war directly behind her passed the mouth of the Patuxent and started upstream. Obviously the commodore of the fleet was proceeding cautiously, afraid his vessels might run aground in shallow water.

The colonel in command of the American regiment watched them from his observation post on the crest of a wooded hill and could not conceal his dismay. "We need cannon of our own," he said to the major, who had just joined him. "With a few big guns, we could blow those ships to pieces. But we have nothing, and they know it. No wonder they're so blasted brave. They know we don't own a single twenty-four pounder, and even if we did, our boys wouldn't know how to use it."

"What targets they make out there," the major muttered, clenching his fists. "How I'd love to smash them to kindling."

For a few moments they watched the enemy's progress in grim silence, and the colonel shook his head. "One of these days the tide will turn. It must. We didn't win our independence just to become helpless colonies again."

His junior spread his hands in a futile gesture. "Muskets won't stop this strong a force. It's like fighting them with our bare hands."

The colonel tugged at his gold-braided bicorn hat. "That's how we did it at the Battle of Long Island in the other war. Yes, and all through New Jersey, and in all the months before the winter at Valley Forge. It was there that we took our stand. We realized we had to win—or perish. Somehow we've got to give these youngsters that same spirit."

"But how, sir?"

"If I knew, President Madison would make me Secretary

of War. Oh-oh! The fireworks are going to start! Pass the word to all companies, Major. Tell them to hold steady!"

A signal was hoisted to the topgallants of the mighty British flagship, and the other men-of-war responded at once by raising colored pennants of their own. Commands were called from the quarterdecks, and the sound of British officers' voices rolled across the open Maryland countryside.

Some American militiamen sensed their danger and crouched low behind their earthworks, checking their muskets and preparing for action. Others, more naive, continued to stare glassy-eyed at the mammoth floating fortresses.

Then, suddenly, thirty-seven cannon on the port side of the *Invincible* roared simultaneously. There was a bright, blinding flash of fire, a small cloud of white smoke appeared, and then a deafening roar filled the air, followed by columns of black smoke that billowed high toward the clear summer sky.

The Americans watched in fascination as heavy iron cannonballs slashed deep furrows in the soft earth.

Lieutenant Harry Greene laughed. "They's firing short, boys!" he called reassuringly. "Lobsterback gunners plain don't know how to aim!"

He spoke too soon. Volleys from the second and third ships-of-the-line came much closer, and then the lead ship found the range. Heated iron missiles plowed through the breastworks as though they were made of paper, destroying in a few seconds the defenses that had taken so many hours of back-breaking labor to build.

Panic swept through the ranks of the militia, and untried soldiers bolted. Soon scores were racing toward the rear.

"Hold firm, boys!" Captain Shoemaker called again and again. He tried beating at his men with the flat of his sword, but to no avail. Other officers tried similar tactics, cajoling and cursing, pleading and threatening, but the young militiamen were too frightened to listen and continued to fall back. The officers went with them, still trying to instill some spirit into them, and not until they approached the tiny village of Bladensburg, about five miles from Washington City, was order restored. There the lines were formed again, panic subsided, and the men forgot their fears—for the moment, at least—and were able to laugh at their own folly.

Bladensburg was the headquarters of General Winder, and several thousand troops began to concentrate there as messengers carried the word to scattered units that the capital of the United States was threatened. Two regiments from Maryland were on hand, with another from Virginia. There were independent battalions from both states and a scattering of companies from Pennsylvania, Delaware and New Jersey.

In theory, Winder commanded enough men to make a strong stand. But observers from the War Department shared the doubts of young officers like Captain Shoemaker and Lieutenant Greene. Almost without exception the troops were militia recruits who had had only a few weeks of sketchy training. All were allegedly infantrymen, and the command desperately lacked artillery support.

There were cheers when three cannon were dragged down the main street of Bladensburg, but the officers were unimpressed. "Those guns were used as decorations on courthouse lawns," Captain Shoemaker said. "They're relics of the Revolution and haven't been fired since the Battle of Yorktown in 1781, thirty-three years ago."

Lieutenant Harry Greene shared his doubts. "Nobody in this brigade knows how to use them. And I'm afraid they might explode and kill their crews when they're fired."

Shoemaker made a valiant effort to see the bright side of the situation. "If they'll give the men more heart, more confidence in themselves," he replied, "these museum pieces will be worth their weight in gold."

Meanwhile, as the Americans dug in for the stand that

General Winder ordered them to make, the British invaders landed unopposed on the banks of the Patuxent. Boats were lowered from the troop transports while the guns of the men-of-war continued to dominate the countryside. Light infantry were the first ashore, assault troops who were experts in mounting barricades and other obstacles. These hardy veterans had gained their experience fighting the divisions of Napoleon in Spain and were accustomed to climbing mountains, fording rivers and, when necessary, fighting from house to house in crowded cities and towns.

They were followed by the heavy infantry, big men wearing breastplates of steel and carrying the most powerful muskets ever manufactured. Members of famous regiments with traditions hundreds of years old, these burly veterans had never lost their heads in battle, never panicked and rarely retreated. "They are ruthless," one of their defeated European foes had written after a vicious battle. "They expect no mercy—and they give none."

Special barges brought the horses of the cavalry squadrons ashore, each trooper standing beside his high-spirited mount. These units were the true elite of the British army, and they had good reason to be proud of themselves and their achievements. They were flexible, capable of demonstrating great speed and, as their French foes in Europe had said, seemed to be everywhere at once when a fight had begun.

The last combat troops to land were the artillery, and several kinds of cannon were unlimbered. There were twelve- and fourteen-pound guns, capable of ripping great holes in the strongest brick walls. Their iron balls, when heated, could start fires that would utterly demolish whole houses, office buildings, and even forts of thick stone. Smaller cannon, ranging from little three pounders to the guns-of-all-work, nine pounders that could be carried forward by teams of three men rather than moved on horse-drawn carriages, had seen action for years against France. And the men who fired them had become such experts that their sergeants boasted they could aim with greater accuracy than infantry marksmen.

Perhaps the most terrifying of all the weapons in the British arsenal were the light howitzers, cannons with long, almost elegantly slim barrels that fired their heated shot high into the air. These balls came down on enemies seemingly out of nowhere and had been known to demoralize some of the toughest battle-hardened veterans.

The British traveled in great style. Quartermaster wagons carried an infinite variety of foodstuffs, blankets, tents and other supplies that made it possible for the regiments to live comfortably in the field. Generals came ashore with huge cartloads of furniture, including four-poster beds and upholstered chairs, leather-topped desks and fine china, crystal and silver for dinner parties. No detail had been overlooked by the War Office in London, which had never forgotten the humiliation of Lord Cornwallis' defeat by General Washington and his "rabble" at Yorktown. This time the British were taking no unnecessary chances and were doing everything in their power to insure a lasting victory.

And so, for the second time in the lives of mature men, Redcoats invaded American soil. For the second time, a land that had once belonged to the British Crown was being dominated by British force of arms.

The Americans had hastily erected new defenses at Bladensburg. Breastworks reinforced with tree trunks and fence posts that had been literally ripped from the ground formed a barricade. Old furniture had been piled on top of the mounds to impede the progress of the enemy, and the militia moved into the line to take its stand. The few officers with experience formed their troops in ranks three deep behind the earthworks, and hard-working sergeants made certain that every musket was ready for use. Spare ammunition and gunpowder were distributed. Someone remembered Napoleon's maxim that soldiers fought better on full stomachs, and quartermasters appeared with loaves of bread and jerked beef brought to Bladensburg from Washington City.

Here and there voices were lifted high in song, and the favorite was "Yankee Doodle," the old battle cry of the Revolution. The untried American militia were as ready as they would ever be.

In the distance they heard drums beat a steady, rhythmic tattoo, and the vibrant calls of bugles echoed through the quiet streets of Bladensburg. Suddenly, on the main road leading into town, cavalry in scarlet tunics, white breeches, and polished black boots led the vanguard of the attacking force. Burnished helmets gleamed in the summer sunlight and plumes bobbed as the horses trotted forward in straight, close lines. A command was shouted, and the riders drew their curved, double-edged sabers, executing the maneuver with such precision that the inexperienced Americans shivered.

Behind the cavalry marched the Redcoat light infantry, bayonets fixed, the men keeping perfect step as their boots pounded on the dusty road. Then, eight abreast in company formation, came the cream of the British army, the heavy infantry, their powerful muskets ready for instant use. Their flag bearers held aloft the eagles they had captured from the French. These standards were enough to strike terror in the hearts of their foes, for they were reminders that the veterans who had served with the great Duke of Wellington in France and Belgium and Spain had won the right to be called the finest fighting men on earth. Apparently they didn't know the meaning of fear, and Lieutenant Harry Greene, studying them through field glasses, thought they actually looked contemptuous.

Light artillery brought up the rear of the long British column. The wheels of howitzer carriages rumbled on the rutted dirt road, and the mule drivers shouted in cadenced unison.

Militiamen from Maryland and Delaware, Virginia and Pennsylvania, peered at the enemy from behind the earthwork barricades, and ripples of apprehension swept through the ranks. Worried officers saw the concern in the eyes of their men and tried to calm them. "Your fathers beat Lobsterbacks in battle after battle. You can do it, too, boys!"

The nervous militiamen were not reassured.

The commanders of the American regiments and battalions had been conferring with General Winder at a headquarters post set up in the Bladensburg post office. Together they had worked out a plan of action that offered them their only real hope of success. If they struck first, with enough force to jolt the British, the frightened Americans might realize their foes were ordinary mortals, not invincible, super-human giants. Then, perhaps, the militia might hold their ground when the enemy counter-attacked.

Orders were carried from headquarters to company officers. Captain Shoemaker, Lieutenant Greene, and all the others of their rank wasted no time. "Make ready!" they shouted. "That's it, boys! Find your targets, but don't be in too much of a hurry. Steady, now. Fire!"

A ragged volley sounded, but the American effort was doomed from the outset. The marksmanship of the militiamen was so inferior that most of the shots went wild. Only a few bullets grazed the riders and their handsome mounts.

The British replied to the challenge at once. The cavalry squadrons increased their pace to a trot, then a slow canter, and the riders whirled their sabers over their heads. The light infantry ran forward close behind them, bayonets aimed straight at millhands and farm boys, clerks and artisans.

Howitzers whined. Shells screamed through the air in a

high arc and exploded behind the American positions, digging deep holes in the ground and kicking up fountains of dirt.

Here and there platoons and even companies of defenders fought valiantly, pitting stubborn courage against the experience of their foes. Shoemaker and Greene had good reason to be proud of their company now. Their men fired, reloaded, and fired again. But the small minority fought in vain.

Most of the militia units were incapable of stemming the British surge. The cavalry slashed through the prepared positions, their trained horses leaping over the barricades. Light infantry climbed over the parapets, bayoneting expertly. And the heavy infantry behind them opened a steady, deadly fire.

The American officers made a final, desperate effort to rally their troops. But panic deafened the militiamen. Everyone was intent on saving his own life, and no one realized that the only way to survive was to stand together. The ranks of the inexperienced Americans broke, and the few units that were giving as good as they received were forced to retreat with the rest. Lieutenant Harry Greene wept, bitterly and unashamedly, but there was nothing he could do to halt the scarlet tidal wave.

In what seemed like no time at all, the discipline in the militia units broke down. Citizen-soldiers were transformed into a panic-stricken mob. The defenders fled for their lives, scattering in all directions. General Winder barely escaped capture and was led away by two of his aides. Colonels and majors followed their men, still pleading, but their voices were drowned by the sound of musket fire and the scream of howitzers.

The rout was so complete that the British made a joke of it. Their buglers played hunting calls, and cavalry squadrons playfully chased terror-stricken militiamen across the fields.

Here and there a young militiaman halted and, in spite of the odds against him, fought ferociously.

But few lives were lost, and the debacle was such a disgrace that the Redcoat high command contemptuously referred to the engagement as "the Bladensburg races."

Captain Shoemaker tried to round up men from any unit he could locate, hoping he'd be able to make a better, more successful stand. But the hysterical militiamen wanted no more of war. No matter what might happen to their country, they were too frightened to stand up to the mighty British legions again.

The invaders took possession of Bladensburg, and not one fighting man opposed them.

General Winder knew his name had been blackened for all time, and he stared blankly into space as his aides led his horse toward the interior.

"It isn't your fault, sir," one of the young men told him. "You weren't given real soldiers. Boys who know nothing of war can't be expected to put up a battle against professional fighting men."

"You mustn't blame yourself, sir," the other aide added hastily. "You've had no field experience yourself."

Winder stirred in his saddle. "The War Department gave me the assignment," he said in a dull voice, "because there was no one else available to take it. They gave me those poor, frightened boys because we have no soldiers anywhere in the area."

In the distance, behind them, they could hear the clear notes of the British bugles, the occasional explosion of a howitzer shell as the artillery fire gradually slacked.

Winder was so overcome it was difficult for him to speak. "Never in our history," he said in a choked voice, "has American pride sunk so low. Only the Almighty knows what will happen to the United States now."

It was unnecessary for him to explain. The aides knew all

too well, as he did, that Washington City was helpless. The
enemy could advance on the nation's capital any time they
pleased and destroy it at their leisure.

A nightmare had become a reality. Washington City, the
young center of a young nation, the symbol of liberty and
human dignity, was doomed.

CHAPTER TWO

Long lines of refugees streamed north, south, and west on every dirt road leading from Washington City. Senators and representatives carried files bulging with papers too precious to be left behind. Supreme Court justices tried to maintain their dignity, but like the humblest of private citizens, they were covered with dust. High-ranking officials of every Executive department were forced to forget their pride, their bright dreams for the future of a nation they loved.

Here and there someone rode, but only a few were fortunate enough to own horses that could be spared. Most mounts had been pressed into service as pack animals and were laden with files the government didn't want to be captured by the enemy.

The majority of the refugees walked, some carrying household goods and family mementos that could not be replaced. A very few had sacks of food slung over their shoulders, but these edibles soon disappeared. Walking was hard work, everyone was hungry, and the limited supplies were shared.

A few women and small children were lucky and rode in mule carts that were also being used to transport documents. Many wept, but their tears were unheeded. Infants cried aloud, and their mothers tried to comfort them, but even the tiny babies seemed to realize that something ominous was in the air. In this hour of great national tragedy, everyone grieved, and in their sorrow the refugees from Washington City were united.

In the capital itself, the confusion was almost indescribable. Cabinet officers and their immediate subordinates continued to race in and out of the recently constructed government buildings, trying to salvage more of the papers that were the sinews of government, the bonds that held the young nation together. At the State Department, correspondence with American legations abroad was dumped into carts. Trusted officials stuffed papers inside their shirtfronts, papers dealing with secrets on which the security of the nation depended. At the Treasury and War Departments, harried men were equally busy, equally frantic. The enemy was approaching, and every minute was vital.

At the Capitol, senators and congressmen who had not already left worked feverishly, too. Among them were the "War Hawks," the brilliant young representatives who, according to New Englanders bitterly opposed to the war, were responsible for dragging the United States into a "senseless conflict." These men were aware that the New Englanders would hold them to blame for the tragedy, but they still believed they were right. Their expressions were grim, but they refused to give in to despair.

Henry Clay of Kentucky and Felix Grundy of Tennessee, John C. Calhoun of South Carolina and a dozen others hastily filled saddlebags with the papers they believed most important to enable the legislative branch of the government to function elsewhere.

Then, their faces ashen, they mounted their horses and rode together in a silent body toward the west. Without exception they carried firearms, the Westerners holding frontier rifles across their pommels, the Southerners with pistols jammed into their belts. If necessary, these men, the elected representatives of the American people in the Congress of the United States, were prepared to defend the honor of their country and their own personal integrity, no matter what the cost.

They were determined, too, that the democratic form of government created and developed by the men who had declared America's independence would not disappear from the earth. Like the patriots of that earlier generation, the young congressmen were idealists. They were dedicated to the principle of self-government, to the theory that all citizens should have a voice in government. Now their dedication was being put to its most severe test.

Baltimore would be menaced after helpless Washington City fell to the enemy. A tide of scarlet might sweep over Philadelphia and New York and Boston. So, if need be, the congressmen were prepared to establish a new capital west of the Appalachian Mountains. There, if they had no choice, they would gird for a war that might continue for decades— until true freedom was won.

The last major center of government in Washington City to be evacuated was the Executive Mansion, where dignity and order had given way to sheer bedlam. Staff members and secretaries filled coaches with documents vital to the security and welfare of the whole country. Papers from the administrations of Washington, John Adams, and Thomas Jefferson were dumped without ceremony into carts and hauled away. Hoarse, frenzied men threw bundles from upper-story windows, bumped into each other in corridors, gave commands and then contradicted themselves.

Throngs of aides worked feverishly in the yards and gardens, trampling on recently planted rose bushes, crushing geraniums that had been Mrs. Adams' favorite flowers. They labored to remove every scrap of paper, every file that might be of any value to the enemy.

The calmest person was a handsome, gracious woman, believed by many to be the most beautiful and charming in the land. Dolley Madison, the First Lady of the United States, was quietly and efficiently supervising the loading of treasures that were already a part of the young nation's growing heritage. At her direction portraits of the first three presidents were packed and placed in a carriage, together with books each had left to his successors in order to form the nucleus of an Executive Mansion library. She herself stuffed clean, soft rags around a marble bust of Benjamin Franklin that had been made in Paris when the great Pennsylvanian had been the American envoy there. And she watched carefully as the box containing the bust was deposited in the carriage.

Then she darted into the house, holding her full skirt and petticoats above her ankles, emerging a few minutes later with a handsome silver tea service that had belonged to Abigail Adams when her husband had been President. She told four men where to find the desk President Jefferson had used and, when they carried it onto the lawn, covered it with a linen sheet so its exquisite leather-tooled top would not be scratched or marred when it was placed upside down in a cart.

"Find the silver ink jar that President Washington's Cabinet gave him when he began his second term," she told a secretary. "It was inscribed, and the British would love to exhibit it in London as a trophy. While you're about it, don't forget President Adams' small-sword. It hangs on a wall just outside the family quarters on the second floor, and the sheath bears an inscription from the Massachusetts General Court. Then there's the tureen in the dining room that John Hancock had made for General Washington. We mustn't leave it behind, either."

A young officer of the Presidential Honor Guard hurried up to her, perspiration streaming down his face. "Ma'am," he said, "you've forgotten your own clothes—and the President's. Tell me where they are, and I'll send a squad upstairs for them."

"Don't waste time on our personal things," Mrs. Madison replied. "There isn't space for them, nor time to take them."

The officer started to protest.

She cut him short. "Get Mr. Jefferson's china instead, and his lovely wine-racks. Oh, and don't forget the watercolor of the Washington estate at Mount Vernon. Americans can enjoy looking at it for many generations to come, and I don't intend to let it fall into British hands."

Mrs. Madison's calm was matched only by that of her husband. James Madison, fourth President of the United States, looked almost insignificant at first glance. He was short and slender, with delicate features, and his political enemies had tried to ridicule him by insisting that a strong wind would blow him away. But his personal courage in the face of certain catastrophe was extraordinary.

He sat in his office with his Secretary of State, tall, lugubrious-looking James Monroe, and both appeared completely relaxed, as though this were a normal, routine day. Every few minutes their conversation was interrupted by another messenger, and the couriers arrived in a never-ending stream to report that the strong enemy column was drawing closer to the city. But the President merely nodded, smiled, and continued his talk with his principal assistant.

The vital presidential files had already been removed, and when a secretary came in to empty the Chief Executive's desk, Madison quietly moved to a chair on the far side of the office. But his manner became severe when a major arrived from the War Department with a hastily scribbled note.

"My compliments to the Secretary of War," he said. "Please inform him I must decline his offer of an additional escort. The Honor Guard Company affords me and my family ample protection."

"Forgive me for contradicting you, Mr. President," the worried officer said, "but I think you'll change your mind when you see this dispatch."

Madison accepted the sealed report but did not open it. "You might also tell the Secretary of War," he added dryly, "that any troops capable of hitting a Redcoat with a musket can be far better employed on the approaches to Washington City than they would be hovering over me." He waved the major away, then opened the communication.

Monroe was astonished when the President chuckled. "What are you so confounded pleased about?"

"Look at this, and you'll see."

The Secretary of State scanned the report. "The War Department estimates that a maximum of four thousand British troops have accompanied the fleet."

Madison's smile broadened. "It's good news, James. From what we heard initially, a tremendous army had been landed in Maryland."

"I'm blamed if I can understand why this is *good* news! Four thousand enemy troops can do a great deal of damage, Mr. President!"

"So they can, unfortunately. But it isn't a large enough corps to attempt a permanent occupation of Washington City. They're raiders, James. They haven't come to take ground and hold it."

Monroe thought for a moment or two, then nodded. "I dare say you're right."

"I'm convinced this attack on Washington City is a diversion, nothing more. The British want to humiliate us in the eyes of the world, to be sure. But the real purpose of the fleet's appearance in Chesapeake Bay is to attack Baltimore and destroy our merchant fleet there. London knows the only way we truly can be forced to our knees is by destroying our shipping."

"Of course. And this report confirms the earlier estimates."

"I've already notified our Army and Navy commanders in Baltimore, alerting them to the danger, and this dispatch from the War Department says that a copy has been sent to Baltimore. So we won't be caught by surprise there."

"That's comforting." Monroe hesitated before speaking his mind freely. He had been the President's friend and close associate for a long time, but no man dared to point a too sharply accusing finger at the elected chief of the American people. "I hope I'm wrong, Mr. President. But it seems to me that you're—well, taking this humiliation rather lightly."

"You're dead wrong, James," Madison said, his face sobering. "Our militia regiments weren't equal to the task they were given. Had we been able to put trained soldiers in the field, the story might have been different, but our real troops are scattered on a dozen fronts. The militia flight is a tragedy, and another is to come. I'm afraid the British may inflict great physical damage on this city. But I refuse to waste my substance. I won't squander sentiment regretting what can't be helped or avoided."

As usual, his cold logic made complete sense. Some men said that ice water ran in President Madison's veins, but no man in public life was more efficient, and a flicker of admiration appeared in Secretary Monroe's eyes.

"They're certain to withdraw after they've defaced a few buildings and otherwise conducted themselves like barbarians," Madison continued. "What they don't realize—and what we must never forget—is that we have millions of acres of forest wilderness in this country. In those forests is enough wood to rebuild Washington City a hundred thousand times, if need be."

"It's true," the Secretary of State said reflectively, "that we're only evacuating our capital temporarily."

"And that's what matters! You'll recall that George Washington lost Philadelphia when it was our capital during the War of Independence. But he regained it. The British couldn't hold it, any more than they can hold this town. We'll return, far sooner than anyone imagines possible." The President thumped the arm of his chair for emphasis. "We're engaged in a brief tactical retreat, but there's no reason for thinking our world has come to an end. We shall continue to fight this war until it's won! I make that an unconditional promise to the people of the United States!"

An urgent knock sounded at the door, interrupting him. An instant later Captain Robert Talbot, commander of the Honor Guard, came into the office without waiting for permission. "Mr. President," he said vehemently, "the enemy vanguard will arrive here in a quarter of an hour."

Madison remained expressionless and calmly consulted his gold pocket watch. "Thank you for the information, Talbot. I shall keep it in mind."

"Sir," the desperate officer declared, "there isn't one American musket between them and us!"

"I understand, Talbot." The President turned back to his Secretary of State. "In the long run, James, this attack will help rather than hurt us."

"How, Mr. President?"

"The New Englanders who have been opposed to the war —who have been calling it 'Mr. Madison's War'—will finally understand that all Americans must support our effort—or perish. As Jefferson has said so often, and you've heard him say it, we actually need a national tragedy to arouse the consciences of the short-sighted."

Monroe hunched forward in his chair. "Thinking of it in your terms, Mr. President—and it's the only sensible way, I'll admit—this whole miserable business should help us in other parts of the world, too. The British like to picture themselves as civilized, but they're making a blunder by attacking a defenseless city. They're driving our women and children out of their homes. Other countries will say that Britain is a land of barbarians. I'll have a few quiet chats myself with the various legations here. After we return, of course."

Captain Talbot looked first at the President, then at the Secretary of State. Neither seemed in the least concerned about the approach of the Redcoats. A mere captain could not give orders to his commander-in-chief, and Talbot realized he badly needed reinforcements.

He bolted, ran out onto the lawn, and finally found the First Lady. "Mrs. Madison," he said desperately, "please, ma'am. I've got to have a private word with you."

Dolley Madison completed her instructions regarding the removal of the flat silver before giving him her attention.

"Ma'am," he said, "the enemy cavalry will be here at any moment. I've already told the President, but he and Secretary Monroe are sitting in there talking about affairs of state as placidly as you please. Listening to them, you wouldn't know they might be captured by the Lobsterbacks and dragged off to London in chains!"

"Dear me," Dolley Madison said mildly. "We can't allow that to happen, can we, Captain?" Refusing to become flustered or upset, she walked into the Executive Mansion with Talbot close behind her.

Secretary Monroe rose to his feet as she came into the inner office, and the President finally stood, too, looking faintly surprised. "I didn't know you were still here, my dear," he said.

"I've been waiting for you, Jemmy," she replied in the same even tone.

"Very thoughtful of you, but I'm not sure Washington City is the safest place in America for a lady at the moment."

"It's as safe for me as it is for the President of the United States." She returned his bland smile. "In other words, I know of no place more dangerous. It's time for us to leave."

He took his watch from his pocket, then shook his head.

"There are one or two matters of some urgency that I want to discuss with Secretary Monroe."

Captain Talbot looked as though he wanted to throw the diminutive President over his shoulder and carry him out of the office.

But Dolley Madison was equal to the emergency. Understanding her husband thoroughly, she preferred the indirect approach to the problem. "I was told your family left a half-hour ago, Mr. Monroe."

The Secretary's mind was on the nation's business, too, and he nodded absently.

"Why don't you ride with us?" she continued. "Then you and the President can continue your conference. Unless you think I might be in the way."

"Hardly, Mrs. Madison!" The Secretary of State bowed. "I'd be honored."

To the infinite relief of Captain Talbot, Mrs. Madison took her husband's arm and firmly guided him to their waiting carriage.

The President handed her in, he and Secretary Monroe followed, and the troops of the Honor Guard quickly surrounded the coach. Talbot weighed the odds against them and was still concerned. The members of his company were experienced cavalrymen capable of dealing with a limited crisis. But not even the most efficient and courageous troopers on earth could cope with an enemy who outnumbered them by odds of forty to one.

"Drive like fury!" he instructed the Presidential coachman. "And no matter what happens, don't stop! If the Redcoats come after us, my men and I will fight a delaying action. See that you use every second. President Madison must not be captured by the British. Even if he doesn't care about his own safety, it's our duty to see that he escapes. The United States is going to need him more than ever in the months ahead."

His sword drawn, Talbot pointed toward the northwest, and the coach bounced and swayed on the rutted dirt roads, the team of matched bays cantering by the time they had pulled the carriage a short distance from the Executive Mansion. For approximately five minutes the Captain, riding ahead, pressed forward through streets that were now virtually deserted. The British would find Washington City a ghost town.

Behind the little cavalcade a cloud of dust rose from the direction of Pennsylvania Avenue, an almost sure sign that the Redcoat cavalry was approaching the Executive Mansion. Talbot coaxed the column to attain greater speed, even though the distinguished occupants of the coach were being subjected to a jarring, uncomfortable ride.

In years to come, he thought, people would find it difficult to believe that President Madison and his Secretary of State, the two most important men in the United States, had escaped from the enemy by no more than an eyelash. Perhaps they had been foolhardy by taking such a great risk, and yet their steel nerves, their total disregard of personal danger were significant. A nation led by such men would never admit defeat, no matter how bleak the country's situation.

Talbot offered a brief but fervent prayer of gratitude to the Almighty when the party reached the open countryside. No British pursuers were anywhere in sight, and it appeared that the President's gamble had succeeded. But the Captain took no unnecessary chances and maintained the same steady pace.

Two hours later, after a wild and hectic ride, the party finally reached the little town of Rockville, Maryland. Two regiments of experienced Pennsylvania militia had already arrived under forced march, and several squadrons of elite Virginia and Maryland cavalry soon followed. New cannon from a nearby foundry were hauled into place, dominating the road to Washington City, and were manned by veteran artillerymen. Talbot breathed more easily, and so did members of the Executive staff who had preceded Madison to Rockville. The personal safety of the President was at last assured.

The owners of the only inn in the town, now the temporary capital of the United States, offered to turn their entire establishment over to President Madison, but he reproved them gently. "Mrs. Madison and I require only one small room," he said. "And when Mrs. Monroe joins the Secretary this evening, their needs will be the same as ours. Too many of our people are homeless today for any man to be greedy, no matter how high his place. In this hour of mutual sorrow, we must share what little we have."

The Honor Guard borrowed a tent from the Pennsylvania militia, and erected it on the lawn of the inn, and there James Madison established his working headquarters. His desk was a board held up by two empty barrels, he and his visitors used plain, straight-backed chairs of unpainted pine, and as there were few oil lamps in the little town, illumination was provided by home-made candles. The President gave no sign that he was even aware of the inconveniences, and his manner and his bearing remained impressively dignified.

He worked steadily, receiving reports from War Department couriers on the invasion, conferring with members of his Cabinet and with senators, congressmen, and other officials who hurried to Rockville in order to be near him. He was so disinterested in food that he refused to eat until Mrs. Madison herself brought him a tray. She was aware of his tension, which he managed to conceal from everyone else, and only when he promised not to neglect his health did she return to the dining room of the inn for her own meal with some of the other ladies.

Late in the evening the President received word that Baltimore was now braced for an invasion. Militiamen in large numbers were arriving in the great port city, the Navy and merchant shippers were working together to prepare for a fight with the powerful British fleet, and small forts elsewhere in the area were being stripped of their cannon. The guns were moved to Baltimore, and the city was ready to give as good as it received.

The President was satisfied that the Marylanders would give a good account of themselves. "There will be no repetition of the panic at Bladensburg," he said.

Midnight came, and an hour later a mounted Virginia militiaman, disguised in civilian clothes, arrived with the first eyewitness report of what was happening in Washington City. "I was there, Mr. President, and I saw it all," he said. "The Redcoats set fire to the Executive Mansion and the Capitol. They lighted bonfires in the State Department and the Treasury and the War Department, too. Every important government building was burning when I left. The only good news is that the wood is so green in some of them that the damage is less than you might imagine."

"Was there any looting?" Madison asked sharply.

"No, sir. The Redcoats were well-behaved and orderly, I've got to say that much for them. They followed their officers' orders, and they didn't get out of hand. Their commanders wanted information from civilians, but none of our people were molested." The soldier forced a laugh. "One of the Lobsterback Generals tried to find out where you had gone. I reckon he was given fifty different answers, none of them the right one."

"Are they still in the city?"

"When I sneaked away, only their rear guard was left, and by now I think it has probably gone, too. The regiments marched from one building to another, setting fires, and then they went off toward their ships on the Patuxent."

The burning of Washington City was a gesture of supreme British contempt and was a stinging humiliation. But the

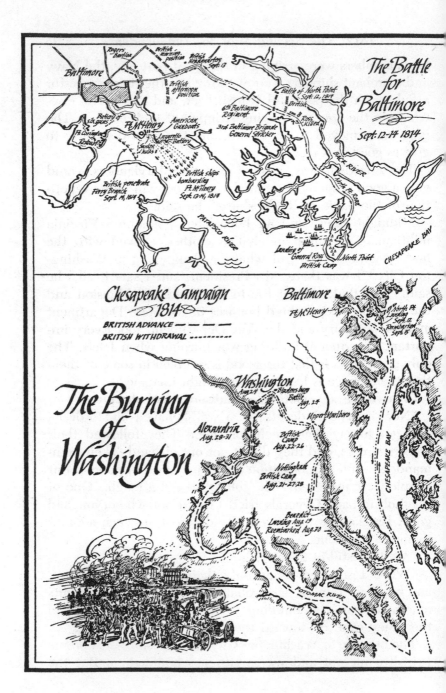

The Battle for Baltimore

Sept. 12-14 1814

Baltimore

Rogers Bastion
British morning position
British Headquarter Sept. 13
British Afternoon position
Battle of North Point Sept. 12, 1814
British
Gen. Ross Killed
6th Baltimore Regiment
3rd Baltimore Brigade General Stricker
Battery of six guns
Ft. Covington
Redoubt
Ft. McHenry
American Gunboats
Lazaretto Batteries
Sunken Hulks
Red Star Line
British penetrate Ferry Branch Sept. 14, 1814
British ships bombarding Ft. McHenry Sept. 13-14, 1814

PATAPSCO RIVER

BACK RIVER

NORTH PT. ROAD

Landing of General Ross British Camp
North Point
CHESAPEAKE BAY

Chesapeake Campaign 1814

BRITISH ADVANCE — — —
BRITISH WITHDRAWAL - - - - - - -

Baltimore
Ft. McHenry
N. North Pt. Landing Sept. 12 Reembarkation Sept. 15

The Burning of Washington

Washington Aug. 24
Bladensburg Battle Aug. 24
Upper Marlboro
British Camp Aug. 22-26
Alexandria Aug. 28-31
Nottingham British Camp Aug. 21-27-28
Benedict Landing Aug. 19 Reembarked Aug. 30

CHESAPEAKE BAY

PATUXENT RIVER

POTOMAC RIVER

President was relieved that his original estimate had been correct. The enemy had no intention of occupying the American capital for any length of time.

After thanking the militiaman, the President went out onto the lawn, accompanied by several of his senior advisers. All of them stared in the direction of Washington City, where a faint, red glow lighted the night sky. Haggard faces reflected the pain of these men who were responsible for the destiny of the beleaguered United States, and at last the President broke the silence.

"This is the beginning, not the end," he said. "The honor of this nation must and will be recovered. Our people have good cause to be united now. We shall work together—and fight together—until Great Britain is made to understand we are no longer colonials but a free and independent people. Then, but only then, will we achieve true victory and lasting liberty."

CHAPTER THREE

"The War of 1812," wrote Thomas Jefferson wryly after the great conflict had ended, "actually began in 1783, on the very day in 1783 that Great Britain recognized the freedom of the United States—or so it seemed at the time." This great American, author of the Declaration of Independence, a founder of the young nation and twice her President, was exaggerating, of course, but there was an element of truth in his irony.

It was difficult for the British to realize that their former colonies were no longer part of their Empire. And after the French Revolution, which began in 1787 and destroyed the monarchy of that great land, France also found it inconvenient to respect the independence and integrity of the New World nation she had helped so generously.

The reason for this lack of regard for the United States by the great powers was a simple one: they were at war with each other. The brilliant Napoleon Bonaparte had made himself master of France and was dominating the whole of continental Europe. Britain, afraid Napoleon intended to invade and crush her, fought furiously for her own existence. And the infant nation in the New World, not yet strong enough to flex her muscles, was caught in the middle of the ferocious combat between the two giants.

As early as 1802 the United States was being humiliated,

and late in that year Robert R. Livingston, the American Minister to France, received instructions from President Jefferson to do something about a situation that had become intolerable. The wealthy Livingston, a tall, suave New York landowner who had helped Jefferson draft the Declaration of Independence, immediately made an appointment with Napoleon's Foreign Minister, the wily Charles de Talleyrand.

They seemed evenly matched as they sat opposite each other in Talleyrand's magnificently appointed office in the ancient Paris residence of French kings, the Louvre. The Frenchman, in an expensive silk suit and a shirt with exquisite lace cuffs, was at ease behind his desk and smiled as he offered his guest a glass of wine. The spare, stern-faced Livingston, wearing unadorned black, calmly refused.

"I can't drink with a man who persecutes my countrymen, Your Excellency," he said.

Talleyrand raised an eyebrow. "You use strong language, *Monsieur*."

"I can't remain silent in the face of repeated outrages, sir." Livingston carefully refrained from raising his voice. "Ever since France recovered her Louisiana territories from Spain, Americans have been made to suffer. You deny our Western states, Kentucky and Tennessee, the right to use the Mississippi River, their natural outlet to the sea. Our Ohio Valley settlers can't send their farm products and lumber and furs down the river. The port of New Orleans is closed to us. Our Westerners are going bankrupt—and will starve unless you reverse your policies."

The French Foreign Minister studied a diamond ring on the little finger of his left hand. "I sympathize with your plight, *Monsieur*, but what can we do? We have no choice." He shrugged. "France is at war."

"Not with us, sir!" Livingston was finding it difficult to control his temper. "Why should American farmers and manufacturers be penalized because France is at war with England?"

"Unfortunately, some American products find their way to the British Isles. They're a proud breed, the English, and they won't sue for peace until they're very hungry. So we can't permit the goods of any nation to reach her shores."

"The United States is an independent nation, Your Excellency. On behalf of my government, I tell you flatly that we resent being told what you will and won't *permit* us to do."

"I am genuinely sorry, *Monsieur*. But in a world where the strong dominate, the weak must do as they are told, is it not so?" Talleyrand smiled. "But do not despair. I take no joy in being insulting to you, and perhaps something can be done to make the situation of your country more bearable."

"Something was done" in the spring of 1803, to the astonishment of Livingston and of James Monroe, who joined him in Paris as President Jefferson's personal envoy. Napoleon, devoting all of his effort and energy to the war against England, offered to sell his vast American territories to the United States. The offer was eagerly accepted, and the vast "Louisiana Purchase," as it was known, added tens of millions of acres to the United States. The young nation now enjoyed the *potential* of becoming strong, a great power in her own right.

But the British, fighting more furiously than ever for their lives, were employing Napoleon's schemes against him. Their fleet, the most powerful in the world, blockaded the Continent. Neutral shipping suffered, and the merchant marine of the United States was subjected to repeated indignities.

It was small wonder that Captain Henry Weysmith, master of the four-hundred-ton brig, *Betsy Ann*, twenty-three days out of New London, Connecticut, was nervous. His destination was Stockholm, the capital of neutral Sweden, and his ship was loaded with a valuable cargo of tobacco, corn and potatoes, a cargo that would bring high prices from Swedish merchants. But he was sailing through the dangerous waters of the North Sea, en route to the Baltic, and knew that the ever-alert British navy was on patrol somewhere in the area.

Perhaps he was overly apprehensive because it was his first voyage into European waters in five years. But friends in New London and Boston and Newport had warned him that the British recognized no neutrality in their struggle for survival. Those who failed to stand with them were their enemies.

Weysmith was eating a breakfast of pickled beef and water-biscuits in his quarters when the cabin boy appeared to announce, "Sails off the starboard bow, Cap'n."

After hurrying to his quarterdeck, Weysmith peered at a squadron of three ships through his glass, and his worst fears were realized. Two of the vessels were sloops of war, which could out-run any merchantman afloat, and the third was a powerful frigate of forty-eight guns. Direct hits by only a fraction of her cannon would be enough to sink him.

As he watched, the frigate hoisted the British flag, and the sloops did the same. All three were bearing down on him, and he had to make a rapid decision. Flight was impossible, and a failure to identify himself would be a virtual guarantee that the British would attack.

"Hoist your pennant!" he ordered his mate, and a few moments later the Stars and Stripes of the United States floated from the topgallants above the mains'l.

"Stand by for boarders," the frigate signaled. Her commander, indicating he meant business, ordered his gunports lowered, and as he swung his starboard side toward the Yankee brig, the muzzles of twenty-four cannon gleamed in the morning sunlight.

Resistance was as useless as an attempt to escape. Weysmith ordered his sea anchor lowered, and his feeling of helplessness increased as one of the sloops maneuvered to take up a position off his stern while the other hovered a quarter of a mile away, off his port side. A longboat was lowered from the frigate, and soon a lieutenant in the Royal Navy, accompanied by eight marines armed with muskets and bayonets, stepped aboard the *Betsy Ann.*

Weysmith waited for them on his quarterdeck.

The lieutenant wasted no time. "Show me your papers and manifest," he demanded brusquely.

The master of the Yankee brig made a vain attempt to maintain his dignity. "By what right do you make this request?"

The British officer laughed. "You colonials have gall."

"Colonials? I am an American citizen, sir, and this is an American ship!"

"Frankly, I don't care what you call yourselves! Your papers, at once!"

Weysmith fumed in impotent rage as the cool, condescending Englishman looked through the documents.

"A jolly good haul," the lieutenant murmured, then added casually, "Your cargo is being confiscated."

Weysmith was stunned. "You have no right—"

The officer's laugh cut him short. "Don't speak to me of your rights, colonial. Can you give me an unconditional promise that the Swedes wouldn't sell this merchandise to the French? Of course you can't. So we're taking no chances."

"As a free American," Weysmith declared, "I needn't answer to you or anyone else. I'll sell where I please."

"You'll do nothing whatever with this cargo. And you're lucky the commodore has enough men in our squadron. If he didn't, we'd impress half your crew. You colonials never know when you're well off, but take my word for it—when you're dealing with His Majesty's Navy, do as you're told if you don't want your nose bloodied!"

The master and crew of the *Betsy Ann* were indeed fortunate. England, hard-pressed for men to stem the tide of Napoleon's victorious forces, had begun to impress American merchant seamen, literally kidnapping them on the high seas and forcing them to serve in the Royal Navy. Monroe, now the American Minister to Great Britain, lodged one formal protest after another. The British listened politely but continued their raids.

Then, in June, 1807, an incident occurred that was destined to create an even deeper misunderstanding between the United States and her former "mother country." A small American frigate, the *Chesapeake*, sailed from Chesapeake Bay, bound for the Mediterranean, where Yankee shipping was being harassed by the pirate nations of the North African Barbary coast. Shortly before sailing she received new armaments, but speed was so essential that Captain James Barron, her commander, was ordered to mount the guns while on the high seas rather than spend precious time performing the task in port.

Shortly before the *Chesapeake* set sail, Admiral G. C. Berkeley, the head of the British naval station at Halifax, Nova Scotia, received a report that four British deserters were members of the American warship's crew. Acting with more zeal than common sense, he immediately dispatched one of his most powerful frigates, the *Leopard*, to intercept the Yankee vessel at sea and seize any British sailors who might be on board.

His specific orders read, in part, "Use any measures necessary to accomplish this mission."

Drama—and tragedy—were in the making.

Less than forty-eight hours after the *Chesapeake* put to

sea, the waiting *Leopard* pounced on her quarry. Both vessels hoisted their flags, in accordance with international law, and the English commander sent his first lieutenant across the waters in a boat.

The unsuspecting Barron awaited the visitor, annoyed by the delay but determined to observe every courtesy. The British officer was piped aboard, and a major of American Marines escorted him to the quarterdeck, where sharp salutes were exchanged.

"Sir," the British officer said, "I am instructed, in His Majesty's name, to demand that you release all deserters from the Royal Navy on board this ship into my custody."

Captain Barron was indignant and a trifle impatient. "I know of no British deserters in my crew," he said honestly.

The visitor drew a sheet of paper from an inner pocket and unfolded it. "I have here a description of the men we seek. Be good enough," he continued imperiously, "to muster your crew for my inspection."

The request was so outrageous that the short, square-jawed Barron reddened. "Do you realize, young man, that you're a foreigner on board United States property? Has it occurred to you that I could no more grant your demand than—than the President would allow you to make a search in Baltimore or Pittsburgh or some other American city?"

American officers and sailors, hearing their captain's spirited reply, grinned happily.

The British officer's expression did not change. "You refuse, Captain?"

"I do," Barron replied firmly. "You'll have to take my word that I know of no deserters from your Navy in my crew."

"I don't doubt your personal word, Captain, but it's possible that you wouldn't know there were British deserters aboard."

Captain Barron shrugged. "Your point is irrelevant. The honor and dignity—not to mention the integrity—of the

United States make it impossible for me to grant your request."

"My commander anticipated such a reply," the British lieutenant said frigidly. "I've been ordered to tell you that you must bear the responsibility for the consequences of a refusal."

Barron resisted the urge to tell him to go to the devil. "Good day," he said politely.

The lieutenant saluted and marched stiff-legged from the quarterdeck.

Barron did not speak until the British officer reached his boat, which started across the sea toward the *Leopard*. "Mr. Martin," he directed the lieutenant from Boston who was serving as officer of the watch, "you may hoist anchor and prepare to resume sail."

"Aye aye, sir!"

Seamen raced to their sailing posts, and Captain Barron walked to the quarterdeck rail, where he stood staring across the water at the sleek and powerful *Leopard*. President Jefferson and Secretary of State Madison would scarcely believe the report he would submit to them, and he wouldn't blame them. It was incredible—almost ludicrous—that a warship of the sovereign United States of America should have been subjected to such a humiliating demand.

The gunports of the *Leopard* had been lowered. The twenty-five cannon on her port side were aimed directly at the *Chesapeake,* and Barron felt a twinge of uneasiness. His own guns hadn't yet been mounted, and, in fact, some were still resting in packing cases, their barrels lined with protective lengths of oiled cloth. He would be helpless if the commander of the *Leopard* carried out the threat implied by the mouths of those twenty-five cannon. But it was impossible to believe that a representative of a civilized nation, at peace with the United States, would carry out such a threat.

The British lieutenant's boat reached the *Leopard,* and

Captain Barron caught his breath when there was a flash, a roar and a heavy iron ball fell into the sea only fifteen yards short of the *Chesapeake's* prow.

All at once the entire British battery spoke simultaneously. The noise of the broadside was deafening, and Barron blinked in astonishment when he saw his mainmast crash and a ball cut a deep furrow in his main deck. His nightmare had come true: the *Leopard* was actually firing on him!

"Mr. Martin!" he shouted. "All hands to battle stations! Mr. Wilson," he continued, barely making himself heard above the tumult as he addressed his gunnery officer, "get some of your cannon emplaced! Step lively!"

The American seamen recovered from their surprise and worked feverishly to prepare the *Chesapeake* for action. Barron ran down to the main deck, where he surveyed the damage, then hurried to the gun deck to help his crew. Officers and sailors displayed heroic courage in the face of overwhelming odds as they tried to move the heavy guns into place.

But the task they faced was too great for them. A second broadside made the *Chesapeake* shudder as British gunners found their target, then a third tore gaping holes in the hull of the American ship. The screams of the dying and the wounded could be heard above the roar of the guns as the white-faced Barron, ignoring his own safety, raced back to his quarterdeck.

"We've suffered a direct hit on the forward hold, sir!" the officer of the watch reported to him.

"Aft hold has sustained a direct strike, Captain," another lieutenant told him.

"Start the pumps!" Barron paced up and down in impotent rage.

A fourth broadside caused the *Chesapeake* to list badly to starboard, and Barron knew his ship couldn't take much more punishment.

Lieutenant Wilson, blood streaming down his face from a cut in his forehead, reported to the quarterdeck, "One gun is in place, sir."

"Then fire at once, Mr. Wilson, for the honor of the flag."

A few moments later the American gun boomed, but the shot fell short.

Captain Barron knew he could wait no longer. "Strike the colors," he commanded, and wept without shame when the Stars and Stripes were lowered.

The worst was yet to come.

The captain and crew of the battered, heaving *Chesapeake* watched in grim silence as a longboat started out across the water again from the *Leopard*, the lieutenant who had visited the Yankee warship previously now accompanied by a strong-armed escort.

A few minutes later the Englishman came on board. "Muster your crew for inspection," he ordered curtly.

Barron had two choices. He could either accept the degradation or, by refusing, go down with his ship. But he couldn't afford to let the United States lose the *Chesapeake*. Her Navy was too small, and every ship was precious.

The tired, smoke-blackened members of the American crew were forced to line the main deck, and only those who had been injured and were being treated by the overworked ship's surgeon were excused. The English lieutenant moved slowly from man to man, studying each carefully as he checked with the description furnished by headquarters at Halifax.

Admiral Berkeley's information proved to be surprisingly accurate. Three Americans who had been impressed in the British Navy and had escaped before joining the forces of their own land were discovered and led away. It was useless for Barron to protest that the kidnapping of his countrymen for service under a foreign flag was both illegal and unjust. Britannia ruled the sea.

A British deserter was found in the American crew, too, and Barron realized that the man had joined him under an assumed name. In British eyes, the vicious raid had been justified.

The longboat returned to the *Leopard* with its victims, and no help was offered to the Yankee frigate which had been unable to defend itself.

Barron began the almost impossible task of trying to make his ship seaworthy again. Carpenters stopped up the holes in the hull, but it was necessary to keep men at the pumps to get rid of the water still seeping in. Auxiliary sails were hoisted to replace some of those ripped to tatters. Finally, convinced that the *Chesapeake* was capable of remaining afloat for a few days, Captain Barron steeled himself and went below to visit the sick bay.

The injured were stretched out on pallets everywhere in the cramped quarters, and the surgeon left a patient for a moment to tell his superior the news that Barron dreaded. "Sir," the medical officer declared, "we've suffered three men killed and eighteen wounded."

The Captain swallowed hard. "When you can, prepare the dead for burial and I'll hold a funeral service. Will the wounded recover?"

"I hope so, sir, with care—and luck. We'll do our best for them."

The Captain made his way back to the quarterdeck and let the brisk sea breeze clear his mind. One major decision remained, but he realized he could not continue his voyage in a badly damaged ship with so many casualties on board.

"Mr. Martin," he said in a choked voice, "make sail for home."

Seventy-two hours later the *Chesapeake* limped into Norfolk, Virginia, and Barron went directly to Washington City as soon as he made certain that the wounded were safely transferred to a hospital.

The entire country was stunned by the outrage. President Jefferson swiftly ordered all British ships in American waters to leave at once. Newspapers wrote blazing editorials condemning the attack and the insult to American honor. Torchlight parades were held in scores of cities and towns, and in Congress speaker after speaker denounced the assault.

When news of the unfortunate affair reached London, the British government, aware that its representatives had been completely in the wrong, offered a swift and voluntary apology. The Foreign Office promised to pay for all damages, including purses for the wounded and the families of those who had been killed.

But Jefferson could not accept such terms. "There's a great principle at stake here," he told his Secretary of State. "Inform the British we insist they abandon the impressment of our seamen. Only when the terror of the press gang disappears can friendly relations between our nations be restored."

Madison faithfully carried out his instructions, but the British balked. Themselves so desperate for manpower in their continuing fight with Napoleon that they could not view the situation clearly, they seemed incapable of realizing that they had no right to force Americans to serve under their flag. For better or worse, right or wrong, they refused the American request.

"Impressments will continue," wrote Monroe, now Minister to Great Britain. "Nothing we say will compel the British to abandon this vile and unfair doctrine—except force of arms. They won't listen to reason, and secretly hold us in contempt. They still think of us as colonials, and will heed our appeals only at gunpoint."

President Jefferson pondered for several days before he read the communication to his Cabinet. "Gentlemen," he told them at last, "I hold the issue of war or peace in my hands. We are too weak to use force to settle this issue, so we must bow our heads for the present. We don't have an Army strong enough to seize Canada and hold it until London agrees to honorable terms. We need time to settle the Louisiana Territory and make it secure. We need time for our new industries to grow and flourish. We need time for settlers in the Ohio Valley to become prosperous.

"So we must buy time for ourselves, and hope that the voices of sensible men of integrity in England will influence the King's government to change its tactics. If we're patient, it may still be possible for the peace to be preserved."

CHAPTER FOUR

Saginaw was a tiny hamlet located on Saginaw Bay, a finger-shaped body of water reaching out from the western shores of Lake Huron. In many ways it was typical of American villages in the West. Some of its residents were farmers who had discovered that crops ranging from cereals to vegetables to fruit trees grew abundantly in the rich, black soil. Some were fishermen who drew an inexhaustible supply of pickerel and lake bass, trout and whitefish from the waters of the bay. A few were fur trappers who earned an excellent living, too, as beaver and black fox lived in vast numbers in the limitless forests that stretched out to the west.

In all, there were forty men, women, and children who made their homes within a radius of five miles of Saginaw. Most were settlers from the eastern seaboard states, a few were immigrants who had traveled west as soon as they had arrived in the New World from England, and two or three were former French Canadians who had moved south rather than accept British rule.

Life was good in this frontier land. Food was always plentiful, and there was an ever-present demand in the established cities of the East for the region's produce. Winters were cold, but the wooden cabins the settlers had built with their own hands were snug, and firewood was plentiful. But a dark shadow hung over the area, as it did over so much of the Great Lakes territories. The people who lived on the shores of Lake Erie and Lake Huron, Lake Michigan and Lake Superior knew all too well that the British claimed the vast region, too.

But governments were far away, and the people of Saginaw lived quietly and worked hard. They would have known complete contentment had it not been for the Terror.

It was always with them, of course, so they couldn't help thinking about it. Not that they talked about it; what was there to say? Everyone knew that the Terror was everpresent, and everyone acted accordingly.

Farmers carried muskets with them into the fields and kept them close at hand. Firearms were as important to the fishermen as their nets and lines, and whenever they sailed close to the shore of the bay or of Lake Huron, they scanned the forest carefully, right hands resting on their muskets.

The women were careful, too. Housewives learned to shoot, and there were pistols in every kitchen. Even the smallest children were taught to respect the Terror. No boy or girl ventured out after dark or wandered alone into the deep woods. They went together to the village school, the older boys carrying muskets which they were prepared to use instantly.

The villagers admitted they had been fortunate—so far. The Terror had never struck the immediate area, but occasionally there had been small, disturbing signs that kept the entire community alert. One evening in the early spring of 1809, soon after James Madison had taken office as President of the United States, Ed Barrows, a Saginaw farmer, saw smoke rising from the forest at the far side of the bay. The next day he and several other men investigated, and near the ashes found a moccasin print in the soft earth.

Bill McDevitt, the trapper, returned from a trip to Fort Detroit two months later with word that the scouts from the American garrison there had been alerted to the presence of warriors from the Ottawa nation in the vicinity. The tribe lived in Canada and rarely traveled so far from home unless trouble was brewing, so people throughout the entire Michigan territory became understandably nervous.

But there was no change in the daily routines of the village on the shore of the bay. Farmers continued to work in the fields, fishermen set out at dawn every morning in their small boats, and the trappers, Bill McDevitt and two others, cautiously searched for game in the forests. Housewives did their many unending chores, the children attended school and helped their parents.

There was reason to hope, in spite of the news about the Ottawa, that the Terror would not strike the village. The local Indians, the Saginaw, who lived nearer the mouth of the bay, had been on friendly terms with the settlers for more than fifteen years. It had become a custom for the warriors to visit the village each year at Christmas, and every summer the people of Saginaw went to the Indian town to share in the feast that followed a ceremony honoring the principal tribal deity, the moon god.

Charlie Elkhorn, a half-breed who was at home in both communities, solemnly assured the settlers that his Saginaw relatives would never be responsible for bringing the Terror to families with whom the savages had been at peace for so long. Everyone wanted to believe him, of course, and the Reverend Mr. White, who came to the village one week in twelve as he made the rounds of frontier towns, offered a prayer for the preservation of peace.

Late one day in mid-summer, the Terror shattered the hopes of Saginaw village. The attack was silent, ruthless, and swift, following the usual pattern of such raids.

Fifteen-year-old Ted Smith was the first to discover what was happening. He had been working in an apple orchard about a mile and a half from home and, his afternoon's work completed, took a shortcut through the deep woods. A sack filled with apples was slung over his shoulder, and he was thinking of supper, a venison stew that his mother and sister had started making that morning. The path took him close to the Barrows house, and Ted decided on a sudden whim to see if Ed Barrows, Jr., wanted to spend a free afternoon fishing with him the following day.

He started toward the Barrows cabin, but something—instinct, perhaps, or a faint, strange sound—made him pause before he emerged from the screen of trees into the clearing. What Ted saw nearly froze the blood in his veins and made his temples pound. Three brawny Indian braves, their naked torsos and faces smeared with the green and yellow warpaint of the Ottawa, were driving the horses from the Barrows barn.

Ed Barrows and his son were sprawled on the ground near the well, staring up at the sky with vacant eyes. Mrs. Barrows lay in a grotesque heap a few feet from her kitchen door. All three had been scalped.

For a moment Ted was too frightened to move. Then he saw two other braves emerging from the house, their arms loaded with kitchen utensils, blankets, and other household goods. A feeling of panic almost overcame the boy, but he forced himself to think carefully. There was nothing he could do for the Barrows family, but perhaps he could help others —provided he escaped without detection.

Ted placed the sack of apples on the ground and crept away, taking care not to step on twigs, dead tree branches, or drying pine cones that would give away his presence. The slightest sound might alert the savages, and the boy was in an agony of fear and suspense. But he kept his head and did not break into a run until he had gone more than one hundred yards. Then he literally raced for dear life, his own and those of others who, with luck, had not yet been attacked.

His first stop was the Henderson house, where the family was just sitting down to supper. Gasping for breath, Ted told them the dreaded news and ran on. He was in time at the Merriwether place, too, and Andy Merriwether started out at once on horseback to alert the families living around the bend of the bay.

At last Ted reached his own home and sobbed aloud when he saw that his parents were still safe. Mr. Smith took charge at once. Carey, Ted's brother, brought the rifles, and Mrs. Smith calmly picked up a loaded pistol. Even eight-year-old Beth was given a pistol, which her father loaded for her.

Then the whole family went into the parlor, which had been constructed like a miniature fort. Its walls were made of thick elm logs capable of absorbing enemy bullets. And on its three open sides were knotholes, large enough for observation purposes—and for the barrels of rifles. The fourth, or "blind" side, which led to the rest of the house, was barricaded.

Candles and the family's one oil lamp were extinguished. Mr. Smith gave each of his sons responsibility for one wall, and himself took a third. Mrs. Smith sat down with Beth in the center of the parlor and quietly started to measure out charges of coarse gunpowder, her fingers moving swiftly and nimbly, even though it was difficult to see in the dark, now that heavy shutters had been nailed into place over the windows.

Tension mounted as the family waited. Outdoors there was no sound except the chirping of a cricket in the underbrush and the cackle of a hen in the poultry pen. Never had Ted known such suspense. He peered out of his knothole over the barrel of his rifle so intently that his eyes watered. Angrily he brushed away his tears, hoping that no one thought him a coward. He couldn't deny he was afraid. After all, he'd seen the whole Barrows family murdered. But he was prepared to do anything necessary and told himself that, no matter how heavy the Ottawa attack, he couldn't afford to flinch.

The wait became interminable. Stars came out, and then a sliver of moon appeared over the bay. Ted could catch just a glimpse of sky through his knothole. Then, suddenly, the wait came to an end. Three burly shadows materialized at the edge of the clearing, past the barn. Behind the warriors were at least four others.

"They're here," Ted murmured. "I see seven of them. On this side."

His father immediately joined him at another knothole on the same wall, then summoned Carey. "Take careful aim, boys," he said. "They outnumber us pretty badly, so make every shot count. Beth, you watch from the other sides to see if they try to surround us."

It wasn't necessary for him to remind his little daughter that braves might sneak close to the house and try to set it afire with burning brands. Even a girl of eight knew what happened when the Terror struck.

Ted looked down the barrel of his long rifle at a warrior who was headed toward the barn. The man was moving very slowly, crouching close to the ground, and made a perfect target. Ted squeezed the trigger, holding his rifle steady.

The Ottawa screamed, crumpled in a heap, and lay still.

At almost the same moment Mr. Smith and Carey opened fire, too. Carey wounded a warrior, and Mr. Smith, a superb marksman, put a bullet through the head of another.

All three reloaded feverishly as the savages opened fire. Eleven-year-old Carey blinked, but recovered his courage when the enemy bullets lodged harmlessly in the thick walls. Mr. Smith and his sons returned the fire with a second round, then a third.

The braves were cautious now, and no one was surprised when Beth called, "Papa." Her voice trembled, but she remained surprisingly calm. "Two of them are coming toward the house on this side."

"Get rid of them, Ted," Mr. Smith directed. "Carey and I will stay where we are."

"All right, Pa." Ted ran to the opposite side of the parlor, and looked out through a knothole.

A warrior was running directly toward him, and looked like a giant. The boy took hasty aim, forced himself to wait until he was certain he would hit his target, and then fired. The Ottawa flung his hands above his head and toppled backward onto the ground.

"Ma," Ted said, an urgent note in his voice, "I need more gunpowder. Quick." His shot had halted the approach of the second brave, but he knew the man would make a dash toward the house at any moment.

"Here you are, dear." Mrs. Smith was as unruffled as she would have been passing bowls of venison stew at the supper table.

Ted reloaded, not wasting a gesture, took a bead on the warrior and fired again. He was annoyed because his shot merely wounded the man, the bullet striking him in the shoulder and spinning him around like one of Beth's tops. But the savage lost all taste for combat and disappeared into the forest, clutching his injured shoulder and moaning.

For another half-hour or more the battle continued. Thanks to Mr. Smith's foresight in making the parlor of his house a little fort, only a few Ottawa bullets penetrated the thick log walls, and they fell harmlessly to the floor, their fury spent. But the settler and his sons took a heavy toll of the raiding party. As nearly as they could judge, they killed six or seven and wounded at least nine others.

At last the Ottawa tired of their beating and withdrew, making an attempt to take their dead with them. But Mr. Smith and his sons kept up a relentless fire, and the savages were forced to leave several bodies behind.

The sudden quiet seemed strange.

"Mama, I'm hungry," Beth said.

Mrs. Smith looked at her husband.

He shook his head. "I'm afraid she'll have to stay hungry for a spell. It may be they'll be back with reinforcements, and it would be too blamed bad for us if they caught us out in the kitchen when they got here. It's far better to be a mite hungry for a few hours than dead for all time."

The night passed slowly. Beth climbed into her mother's lap and slept, but the two boys kept the long vigil with their father. They watched for shadows, for any sign of life in the woods surrounding the clearing where the house and outbuildings stood, but the Ottawa appeared to have had enough.

Dawn came, but Mr. Smith was still reluctant to lower his guard. Then Andy Merriwether appeared, on horseback, and shouted a weary greeting.

"Anybody in there?"

"We're here!" Ted called.

"Come on out, then. It's safe now!"

Mr. Smith followed his son into the open, Carey trailing behind them.

"They've gone," Andy said. "Bill McDevitt followed them early this morning to a spot about ten miles up the bay, where they had their war canoes hidden in rushes. A blame-sight fewer of them went paddling off than showed up here-abouts yesterday," he added grimly. "As near as I can put the figures together, the Ottawa lost at least fifty in dead and wounded."

"How heavy were our casualties?" Mr. Smith wanted to know.

"Well, the whole Barrows family is gone. You already know about them. Seth Davidson was killed, and so were his father and stepmother. And the Haley family got it the worst. The whole family was murdered. Their house was plundered and burned, and all their property taken."

For a moment no one spoke. One fourth of Saginaw's total permanent population had been lost.

Mr. Smith cleared his throat. "Come in for a bite of breakfast, Andy. My wife is putting water on to boil."

"Don't mind if I do, thanks. You're the last on my list to tell the news."

They started toward the house, but Ted remained behind, staring down at the body of a dead Ottawa brave. He picked up the man's musket, studied it, and then called excitedly, "Pa! Andy! Come here, will you?"

"We'll get rid of those bodies after we've eaten," his father replied.

"This is important, Pa." Ted waited until Mr. Smith and Andy joined him, then pointed to a double circle stamped in the metal of the Indian's barrel, near the base.

All three knew the meaning of the mark. The stamp signified that the weapon had been made in Sheffield, England, and was a brand that had for years been used almost exclusively by the Royal Army.

Color drained from Mr. Smith's tired face. The evidence seemed conclusive: the weapons for the raid had been given to the Ottawa by the British.

Ted dropped to one knee and, taking a knife from his boot-top, cut a leather pouch from a thong at the dead warrior's waist. He opened the pouch, then poured its contents into his hand, and felt ill. He was holding a gold half-sovereign and several silver coins of lesser worth. All were English.

"This is real proof," Andy Merriwether said softly, "that the British are inspiring the Terror. They pay the Canadian Indian tribes to make these raids and arm them with the latest British weapons. We've got to do something about this!"

Mr. Smith smiled cynically. "What would you suggest?"

"We'll collect all the muskets and British money we can find. Then we'll send Bill McDevitt to Washington City with it. We've heard long enough that our government can't do anything to stop these raids until President Madison has proof in his own two hands that the British are responsible. Now he'll know—and he'll make King George eat the proof!"

The new British Minister to the United States had not yet arrived in the country, and the acting head of the legation was the counselor, Sir Henry Fowler. He was a dapper, nimble-witted diplomat whom Secretary of State James Monroe had known in London, and Fowler's greeting was cordial as he entered the Secretary's office.

"It's odd that you should send for me today, Mr. Secretary," he said. "Just this morning my wife asked me to invite you and Mrs. Monroe to dine with us later this week."

"If relations between our countries were friendlier, I'd be delighted," the lanky Monroe replied. "But I must be frank with you, Sir Henry. The American people would be resentful if Mrs. Monroe and I were to accept your hospitality under the present circumstances."

The British diplomat was puzzled, but Monroe's attitude as well as his words were a signal that trouble was brewing. Sir Henry braced himself.

The Secretary of State led him to a table at the far side of the spacious office. "I'd like you to examine the exhibits I've gathered for you here."

Sir Henry nodded cheerfully. "Royal Infantry muskets made in Sheffield and a goodly supply of British coins."

"They were taken from the bodies of dead Ottawa Indian warriors after raids on five different communities in the Michigan territory, the most serious of them at a little village called Saginaw."

Fowler's smile faded. "I don't doubt your personal integrity, Mr. Secretary, and I'm sure you present these items to me in good faith. But they could have been misrepresented by the people who brought them to you."

"They were captured by American settlers after five separate and distinct raids, Sir Henry!"

The British diplomat contrived to appear faintly amused. "The weapons could have been purchased by a trader visiting Quebec or Montreal. For that matter, one of your sea captains or merchants could have arranged to buy them in London. As to our coins, it's obvious they're in circulation all over the world. Surely you don't expect me to accept their presence here as valid substantiation of the claim that savages dwelling in Canada were paid by His Majesty's government to raid American settlements."

"That's precisely what I am asking, Sir Henry." Monroe picked up a paper from his desk and handed it to the visitor. "This is an affidavit prepared and signed by a Michigan territory trapper named McDevitt. He started for Washington City from Saginaw with one of the rifles and a few coins and picked up the rest in other villages while on his journey. The story was the same in each place. The Ottawa made sudden, devastating raids, and the evidence was discovered after they either were driven off or withdrew."

Sir Henry became scornful as he glanced at the long, sworn statement. "This fellow appears to have a lively imagination. Let me remind you that many of your trappers cross into our Canadian provinces. There was nothing to prevent him from acquiring both the coins and the muskets there."

"I believe the man, and so does President Madison," Monroe said firmly. "What's more, I'm sure we could get affidavits from all the residents of those villages, swearing that he's telling the truth."

Sir Henry shrugged.

"Do you deny that Crown agents have been paying and arming the savages terrorizing our settlements?"

The British diplomat drew himself to his full height, but was still far shorter than the towering Monroe. "As a repre-

sentative of His Majesty's government, I cannot permit myself to be cross-examined like a common criminal standing
trial for murder, Mr. Secretary!"

Monroe's stare was equally cold and unyielding. "According to accounts I've recently read in several London newspapers, speeches were made by several government representatives in the House of Commons last month on the
subject of our relations. The speakers all talked of 'keeping
the United States off balance.' But they refused to elaborate
when pressed to explain the government's policy. Are these
raids your government's idea of a useful technique to harass
and annoy us, Sir Henry?"

"If you choose to make such an interpretation, I'm not in
a position to stop you, Mr. Secretary."

"I must protest the British policy, then. I do, Sir Henry,
and I warn you that Great Britain will have to accept the
consequences. Personally, on my own behalf, I can't refrain
from adding that I consider such a policy stupidly short-
sighted. You're making enemies of settlers who are the neighbors of your Canadian subjects. Rather than encouraging
peaceful relations, you're stirring up troubles that will keep
the border inflamed for many years to come!"

Sir Henry drew on his spotless white kidskin gloves and
rested a hand on the hilt of his dress sword. "Your American
settlers, Mr. Secretary, have illegally entered His Majesty's
domain. You seem to forget that Great Britain does not admit
the legality of your claim to the Michigan territory. According to our interpretation of the peace treaty we signed with
you in 1783, the entire Great Lakes region is British soil."

"We say it belongs to the United States!"

"You deliberately encourage your rabble to settle there in
the hope they'll obtain squatters' rights."

"And you, Sir Henry, deliberately send savage marauders
to slaughter innocent people, steal their property, and burn
their homes to the ground. If the British government hopes

to frighten our citizens into leaving, then Great Britain learned nothing from the American Revolution. We can't be bluffed or bullied, and no power on earth can force us to abandon our rights!"

Fowler bowed stiffly from the waist. "Good day, Mr. Secretary."

"Good day, Sir Henry." Secretary Monroe stood motionless as the British diplomat stalked from the office. Then he sighed as he picked up his own hat and went to tell President Madison the latest development. It was clear, painfully clear, that England had no intention of changing intolerable policies that were heating American tempers to the boiling point.

How much longer would the United States tolerate the wanton murder of her citizens and the destruction of their homes? James Monroe couldn't answer that question. He knew only that war clouds were growing thicker and more ominous overhead.

CHAPTER FIVE

The weather was unusually warm for southeastern New England in the spring of 1811, and most of the waterfront buildings in the once-thriving seaport of New London, Connecticut, were shrouded in fog. A heavy layer of mist hid the Thames River, too, as fourteen-year-old Tom Garnett and his twelve-year-old brother, Martin, started from their Main Street home to the wharf where their father's fishing boat rode at anchor.

The two boys were intent on spending their holiday from school fishing in Long Island Sound. Their father had granted them permission to use his boat, which was always a treat, and they were thinking only of their outing. Neither was particularly conscious of the air of decay and stagnation that hung over the waterfront even more heavily than the fog. Both boys had grown accustomed to the desolation.

They walked past long rows of empty warehouses which only a few years earlier had been filled with American tobacco and cotton, timber and corn and furs which Yankee merchantmen had carried off to Europe. Other buildings, where goods imported from England and France, Germany and the Baltic countries had been stored, were deserted, too. Most had been boarded up, their owners no longer able to pay even a watchman to stand guard.

There was no sign of life in the shipyard that had belonged to the Garnett family for three generations. The boys made their way past the magnificent trunks of huge oaks which had been trimmed for use as mainmasts and now lay in neglected piles, slowly rotting. They climbed over planks that had been intended for use in the hulls of new merchantmen, but these days no brigs were being constructed in New London—or anywhere else in the United States.

The war in Europe continued to take its toll of American shipping, and only a very few, very courageous shipowners and masters dared to venture into European waters. The English, still insisting that Americans could trade with no one else, seized all vessels they caught sailing for Continental ports. And Napoleon retaliated by capturing Yankee ships bound for England. Only a night or two ago, at supper, Mr. Garnett had said, "The only ports still open to us are in the West Indies. We're slowly being strangled to death, and if something isn't done to relieve us soon, New England will never recover."

The boys climbed on board the boat, and while Tom untied her and hoisted the anchor, Martin unfurled the sail. Nets, which they had carefully mended for their outing, lay at their feet, and their lunch of cold meat and bread, which their mother had wrapped in oiled paper for them, rested in a bucket under the stern seat.

Tom cast off, then took the tiller, and the little craft drifted slowly downstream past the ruins of Fort Griswold, which arch-traitor Benedict Arnold had attacked during his villainous assault on New London during the Revolution. Tom could make out the bare outlines of the fort in the fog, and shivered. Like everyone else in the area, he had been brought up to feel a strong dislike for anything British.

The fog was even heavier in Long Island Sound, but neither of the boys was concerned as their boat moved out of the Thames mouth into the open water. They knew every underwater rock, were aware of the shoals off Fishers Island, which lay off their port bow, and they weren't afraid of the

Sound in a fog. Besides, in another hour or two the sun would burn off the mist.

Martin made the nets secure, then heaved them overboard, and Tom took advantage of a somewhat fresher breeze to sail westward down the Sound toward their favorite fishing grounds, off the mouth of the little Niantic River.

"Go forward," he told his brother, "and keep your eyes open for other boats. This fog is as thick as the porridge that Ma makes for Sunday night supper. We don't want to risk a collision with somebody who doesn't know how to sail."

Martin obeyed, and they sailed in a companionable silence for a time, the craft continuing to pick up speed. Suddenly Martin shouted, "Boat to port."

Tom veered sharply to starboard in order to avoid ramming into a massive object that loomed up directly ahead. Almost too late he realized they were only a few feet from a huge ship.

"You, there!" someone called from above. "Take this line and make fast."

A length of rope crashed onto the deck of the boat, narrowly missing Martin's head.

"Now, identify yourself!" the disembodied voice commanded.

The boys looked at each other in dismay. Both had instantly identified the man's accent as English.

Tom peered up through the fog, and his horror increased as he made out the dim figure of a Royal Navy officer. Nearby were three seamen, all aiming cocked muskets at the pair below.

"Fishing boat out of New London!" Tom's voice was strong and loud. Not for anything in the world would he let the British know he was afraid of them.

A ladder was lowered, and the officer climbed down, jumping the last few feet into the boat.

The one thought that raced through Tom's mind was the

fear that he and his brother would be impressed into Royal Navy service. He looked around for a blunt, heavy object he could use for self-defense, but could find none. If necessary, he told himself, he and Martin could swim to safety. They were no more than a half-mile offshore, a distance they could swim with ease, and it would not be too difficult to shake off pursuers in the fog.

Surreptitiously kicking off his shoes, he faced the officer defiantly and tried, with one hand, to alert his brother with hand signals. "What do you want of us?" he demanded. "And by what right do you board us in American waters?"

The Englishman was amused. "You colonials are a rebel breed from birth, it seems."

"Colonials?" Tom was outraged.

The officer shrugged, refusing to be drawn into a controversy. "We're here by force of arms," he said, and looked mockingly at the stocking-footed boy who was edging closer to the side of the boat. "I wouldn't jump overboard if I were you. The water is cold at this season. And if you're afraid we're going to press you into Navy service, rest assured that we need men, not children."

Even though Tom was relieved that he and Martin were not going to be kidnapped, the insult infuriated him. But he realized he could not afford to antagonize someone being supported by the armed, watchful sailors on the warship's deck and discreetly said nothing more. What did the British want with him and his boat? He literally couldn't guess.

The officer examined the fishing gear, even inspecting the food that Mrs. Garnett had packed for her sons, and then scrutinized the two boys. "You seem to be what you claim," he said, "but I wouldn't put it past Yankees to use children in smuggling operations."

They stared at him blankly, and Martin, swallowing hard, could only repeat, "Smuggling?"

"You Americans have annoyed us long enough with your

refusal to cooperate in our blockade of Napoleon. So we're doing something sensible at last, something we should have done long ago." The officer caught hold of the rope ladder and swung himself onto it. "We've established a total blockade of the entire American coast. No ships may enter or leave your ports without our permission." He started up the ladder, then paused for a moment. "Make certain you do nothing but fish. Use that boat as a go-between for smugglers and you'll be treated to far worse than impressment. Anyone caught disobeying our orders will be sent to an English prison!"

The stunned Tom weighed anchor and quickly cast off. "We'll do no fishing today, Marty," he muttered. "We've got to get home—quickly!"

He tacked expertly and sailed off eastward up the Sound. Soon the haze became lighter, and within a few minutes the boys could see the British warship clearly. She was a sleek, powerful frigate, far larger and stronger than any vessel in the little United States Navy. Her gunports had been lowered, the muzzles of at least twenty cannon were exposed on her starboard side, and it was apparent that she was prepared for instant action.

Martin gaped in ever-increasing wonder.

"Don't just sit there," Tom said sharply. "Haul in the nets, Marty, and hurry." The boat caught the breeze and began to move more smartly.

"Why do we have to go home," his brother asked plaintively.

"Because Pa and Mr. Perry and Mr. Morgan and all the others will want to know about all this. I'm not sure what it means, but I've got me a hunch it's mighty important."

The bronzed sea captains and the older, somewhat portlier shipowners, many of them the former masters of their own brigs, filed into the office of Thomas Garnett, which had been reopened for the meeting. New London seafaring men were always quiet and soft-spoken, but today they were unusually silent, greeting each other with quick, grim nods.

Garnett opened the meeting. "You've all heard why we're here," he said, and repeated the story of his sons' experience in the fishing boat that morning. "Now I'll ask Ed Davis to tell you the rest."

Davis, an unemployed master of a brig who now earned a precarious living as a lobsterman, rose slowly to his feet. "I went out today, soon as the fog lifted," he said in a high-pitched, New England drawl. "I took in the haul from two of my lobster pots, and I was sailing to the third when a longboat from the British frigate out yonder started after me. All at once some sailors started firing muskets over my head. I didn't wait to find out why. I turned tail and came home again."

Winthrop Morgan, who owned the city's largest merchant fleet, hauled himself to his feet. "My brigs have been rotting in drydock, except for two that have been in trade with the Spanish West Indian islands. Do I take it rightly that they'll have to suspend operations, too?"

"It looks that way," Garnett replied.

John Hancock Perry, the most hot-tempered of the group, shouted indignantly, "Let's send a delegation to the Captain of that blamed frigate and make certain."

"I've already gone out there myself," Garnett told him. "I went as soon as my sons brought me the news. The Captain refused to see me, but one of his officers gave me this." He drew a paper from an inner pocket and unfolded it. "It's a Royal Navy decree, based on an act of Parliament passed less than a month ago."

He handed the printed sheet to his companions, who read it in stunned disbelief. The order was very simple: the British Navy, acting under the authority of Parliament, was establishing a total blockade of the American coastline. Yankee merchantmen daring to leave port would sail at their own risk; vessels would be confiscated, their masters would be sent to England for imprisonment, and their crews would be impressed into Royal Navy service.

"This is an open act of war!" Perry shouted.

"Aye, so it is," Morgan declared somberly. "It's what our fathers were forced to endure during the Revolution."

"By what right do they dare?" Perry demanded.

Garnett smiled sourly. "They're acting on their own authority, and we don't have the strength to tell them to go to blazes!"

"If we submit, we'll go bankrupt even faster than we were doing when they blockaded Europe and kept us out of French ports." Perry shook a huge fist, then slumped into his chair. "My brother owns a textile factory. He's been able to keep his head above water in the Spanish West Indian trade, but this will be the end of him, too."

"The government in Washington City will have to do something," Morgan said.

Several men started speaking simultaneously, and Davis made himself heard above the hubbub. "You can't fight frigates and men-of-war with words," he roared in the voice he had used when giving commands from his quarterdeck. "Madison is like Jefferson before him. He'll protest, and that'll be the end of it. I say—to the devil with the Presidents who come from Virginia!"

Suddenly the room was very quiet.

"They have enough food down in Virginia to feed themselves," Davis continued furiously. "But we don't here in Connecticut. Neither do folks in Massachusetts and Rhode Island. We sit here, helplessly, and see our life's work being destroyed. Soon our wives and children will be going hungry. I'm sick of it, and I'm not the only one. If the President and Secretary Monroe—both of them Virginians, mind you— can't make their peace with London and bring this idiocy to an end, I say that New England should secede from the Union and join Great Britain! We have nothing to lose—and everything to gain."

Ed Davis of New London was right when he said that others in New England felt as he did. The region depended on its manufacturing and shipping, and both industries had come to a complete standstill. Thousands of men were out of work and walked the streets in desperation.

Most faced a cruel dilemma. Should they stay at home, where the prospect of finding new jobs was slight? Or should they move out to the ever-expanding West, where land was virtually free and the soil rich—but where British-inspired Indian raids were becoming more violent and frequent with each passing day? Some stayed and soon lost all hope. Others went West and faced dangers and hardships even more terrible than they had imagined.

In Kentucky, Tennessee, and Ohio, the Western states, militiamen were called to active duty to drive off bands of warriors who made life miserable for the settlers. In some of the territories, Michigan and Indiana, Illinois and Wisconsin, Alabama and Mississippi, there was almost no organized resistance to the aroused Indians. Only in Louisiana, which was preparing to ask for admission to the Union as a state, were Indian raiders brought under control and driven out.

New England wasn't the only part of the country that thought of secession as a means of solving its problems. In the West there were wide-eyed dreamers, too. Some thought of forming an alliance with Spain and setting up a government under the Spanish flag. Others, still more impractical, laid elaborate plans to establish their own empires.

President Madison continued to work tirelessly, doggedly for his country, in spite of all that his critics said against him. First, he made a great effort to reach an understanding with

France and Great Britain. Napoleon, aware that he could win American sympathies for his cause at relatively little cost, rescinded his blockade of shipping bound for England. The gesture actually meant very little in realistic terms. The British had become the undisputed masters of the seas, and Napoleon's offer was nothing more than a scrap of paper.

The British remained blind to American interests and sensitivities. American food was needed in England more than ever, because the young men of the British Isles were in uniform, and their elders were unable to grow enough farm products for the country's needs. Arrogantly, stupidly, the British government demanded that America supply her needs.

Madison refused. "Our honor and dignity as an independent, free nation make it impossible for us to bow to such demands," he declared. "If His Majesty's government were to ask us for our grain and fish and meat, and were willing to pay fair and reasonable prices for it, I feel certain we could reach an amicable understanding. But we cannot and will not drop to our knees in response to commands. We reject the order."

London retaliated by tightening its blockade of American ports. Occasionally the master of a Yankee merchantman slipped past the vigilant ships of the line and swift frigates. But these individual feats of daring accomplished little. The total population of the United States was now seven and one-half million people, and trade was needed on a large scale for the country to survive, much less prosper.

The President responded to the contemptuous British move by signing an order forbidding Americans to trade with the former Mother Country. His New England critics were annoyed. "He's cutting off what's left of his nose to spite his face," they said.

Neither they nor anyone else knew that James Madison had no intention of remaining idle, meekly accepting British insults. Afraid that his New England critics in Congress and the Western schemers would raise an uproar if they learned his plans, he acted very quietly. Secret orders went out from the State, War, and Treasury Departments. Men devoted to the preservation of the nation's freedom hitched their belts a notch tighter and went to work.

Even lovely Dolley Madison knew nothing of her husband's activities until late one night in the sultry, hot summer of 1811. The President had gone off to his office very early in the morning, and it was almost midnight when he returned to the living quarters of the Executive Mansion, his face gray, his shoulders slumping wearily.

The First Lady awaited him in the drawing room and hid her concern behind a bright smile. "You must be hungry," she said. "You ate nothing of the dinner I sent down to your office."

"It's too hot," he replied, seating himself near an open window, "and I'm too tired."

Dolley Madison was too wise to argue and, excusing herself for a moment, asked a servant to bring the President a tray of food. She returned to the drawing room to find him staring out of the window at the hastily constructed buildings of Washington City.

"We're a nation dedicated to peace," he said. "We learned the cost of war in the Revolution. No people in this world love peace more than Americans."

He fell silent as the servant entered with the tray.

Mrs. Madison took it and placed it before him. The smoked ham and salad greens came from their own Virginia farm, and the cold fish had been a gift from an admirer. Even the President of the United States and his wife could not afford to eat lavishly these days.

Madison, to his wife's private relief, began to eat absently.

She could not blame him when he grimaced after taking a sip of herb tea. Real tea, imported from India or the Dutch

East Indies, was as scarce now as it had been during the Revolution. And coffee, which came from the West Indies, was equally difficult to obtain. So housewives, even the First Lady, were forced to brew their own tea from the leaves of local plants, and the mixture, at best, was not appealing.

But the President was so deeply immersed in his thoughts that he soon forgot what he was drinking. "In a sense," he said, "I can't blame the New Englanders for their bitterness. Little children are begging for alms in the streets of Boston and Hartford. All but five of the sixty-three factories in New Haven have been closed." He picked up a tiny salt dish and spoon from his tray. "This has become more precious than gold. Do you know what's being charged for salt these days?"

Dolley refrained from replying that it was her business as a housewife to know. "Only yesterday," she said, "I paid two dollars for a container of a few ounces in a Washington City market."

"They're charging three dollars for a small packet in Boston, and the price is still rising." The President sighed deeply. "The same is true of other foods—east of the mountains. A small bag of flour brings five dollars in Philadelphia or New York. But the farmers of the West, who can't afford to transport their produce across the Appalachians, have more to eat than they can use. Wheat and corn are rotting in their warehouses. Is it any wonder that the misguided speak of secession and the establishment of their own empires?"

Dolley seldom discussed affairs of state with her husband, but he wanted to unburden himself, and she was anxious to learn what she could about the country's uncertain future. "Is it really possible that New England will secede and a new nation will be formed in the West?"

"Not while I'm President," James Madison said firmly. "Men are discouraged and confused, but they'll join hands again for the preservation of the United States when they realize that the very existence of American liberty is at stake. I'm relying on a strong reaction in Congress during the next few months to help alert the public to the dangers of extermination we face. And I believe some of the things I've been doing lately will soon arouse men everywhere."

Dolley looked at him questioningly.

The President passed a tired hand across his face. "The news won't be secret much longer. It will begin to leak out in the next day or two. I've contracted for the building of a new Navy fleet, from large frigates to the speediest sloops and most agile schooners of war afloat. In all, I've placed orders for one hundred and seventy-five ships. By next week there will be employment for every man seeking work in our seaports. And that's just the beginning."

The First Lady caught her breath.

"Foundries will be busy turning out cannon and shot. Textile mills will be converted into gunpowder plants. And the Navy is going to open a major recruiting campaign."

"Then you're planning to go to war, James?"

"Unless the British have a change of heart, they give me no choice. I remember all too clearly what we suffered during the Revolution, and I certainly don't want war. But I refuse to let the British gain dominion over us again—while impatient men force various parts of the country to secede. I can see, if they can't, that Britain and Spain are just waiting to gobble up any sections foolish enough to leave the Union."

She slowly twisted a lace-edged handkerchief, so agitated that she was unaware of what she was doing. "Are you going to increase the Federal Army and call up the militia, too?"

The President pushed away his supper tray. "Unfortunately, Dolley, I can't. Not until the Navy becomes strong enough to protect our shores. England is looking for an excuse to declare war against us. If I start to raise a bigger Army, they'll be certain to strike swiftly, before we're able to defend ourselves."

"Won't they consider a larger Navy enough of an excuse?"

"No." The President smiled wearily. "The British like to think of themselves as the only power capable of ruling the seas. They'll be amused, and they certainly won't think of our Navy as a serious threat. They haven't conferred, as I have, with our commodores and captains—the most competent and courageous group of commanders on earth. There are some surprises in store for the Royal Navy, I can tell you."

Dolley rubbed her arms. "I'm shivering."

"I don't blame you. The road ahead is going to be long and hard. First, I'll need strong, voluntary support in Congress. Then, the new Navy will have to hold the British at bay while we train and equip an Army—always a slow and difficult business. I'm afraid the whole country will be forced to make many sacrifices before we'll know peace again. But the alternative is the loss of all that we hold dear."

CHAPTER SIX

The younger members of Congress erupted in anger when Great Britain doubled the size of her fleet blockading the American ports on the Atlantic and sent two squadrons into the Gulf of Mexico to capture merchantmen that dared to sail to or from New Orleans. Most members of the group were Westerners, and one of their acknowledged leaders was the deceptively mild-mannered Henry Clay of Kentucky.

"The patience of this nation has been sorely tried," he told a cheering House of Representatives. "Are we spineless colonials who tug our forelocks and hasten to obey the demands made on us by would-be masters across the sea? We are not! Kentucky was settled by men who loved freedom more than life itself. They love it still and are willing to prove their devotion! Let us show the British lion we don't fear his menacing roar. Let us prove to him, now and for all time, that we are masters in our own house!"

His fervor was equalled by that of short, plump Felix Grundy of Tennessee. "Must we wait, trembling, until Nashville and Louisville have fallen to the British and their Indian allies? Never! Tennessee is ready, at this instant, to send ten thousand of her sons into battle for the sacred honor and liberty of our beloved land!"

Others, among them Richard M. Johnson and Peter B. Porter, spoke in a similar vein, arousing the whole country. Not all of these younger men were Westerners, however.

One who quickly allied himself with them was the scholarly young John C. Calhoun of South Carolina. "Hundreds, perhaps thousands of our fellow citizens are being compelled to serve against their will on board the ships of an alien fleet. They have been drugged and beaten, dragged off at gunpoint. When they try to escape so that they may breathe again the sweet, free air of this, their native land, they are flogged and cast into dungeon cells. Enough!" he cried, and the House roared its approval.

"Let the tyrant be warned," Calhoun continued, "that the United States of America will tolerate no more abuse. Give us back our free sons—or suffer the consequences!

"As for me, I pledge that South Carolina will not falter. Her duty is clear, and she will do it. Blow the bugles, and sound the drums. Liberty is once again on the march."

The most distinguished orator among the younger members of Congress was sedate, Daniel Webster of Massachusetts, whose attitude amply demonstrated that there were many patriots in New England and that not all citizens in that part of the nation were thinking of secession. "Gentlemen," he told the hushed House, "in these crucial times, let the object of our consecrated devotion be our country, our whole country, and nothing but our country. We wear no tags that label us as citizens of Massachusetts or Connecticut, Tennessee or Kentucky. We are Americans, and we ask the help of Almighty God in the task that lies before us.

"We beseech Him to guide and protect us in this, our hour of supreme trial. Confident that we march with closed ranks, wearing the invincible armor of righteousness and brandishing the flaming sword of truth, we shall demolish forever the forces of evil that would humble and enslave us. God grants liberty only to those who love it, and no people on this globe cherish it more than we!"

Newspapers throughout the country published these

speeches, many of which were reprinted in pamphlet form. Americans in every section of the land heeded Webster's inspired words and, abandoning their sectional quarrels, closed their ranks. There were some, particularly in Hartford, Boston, and the other major cities of New England, who opposed the drift toward open conflict with England, but they had become a small minority, and their voices were muted.

Nevertheless it was they who dubbed the belligerent young congressmen the "War Hawks," and the recipients of the title gloried in the name.

"War Hawks we shall remain," Clay declared, "ready to swoop down out of the sky to avenge our nation's shame unless Britain quickly rights the wrongs she does us."

President Madison now had the support he sought, but even he became alarmed as the eager congressmen demanded immediate military action. "They've united the country behind me," the President told Secretary Monroe, "and I'm grateful to them. But they're pushing too hard and too fast. If they don't slow their pace, we'll be at war before we're ready!"

Events were moving swiftly now, too, and although the President hoped to delay the beginning of actual hostilities until his reinforced Navy was ready for sea duty, the British carefully planned to strike the first blow. Rather than openly initiate the fight themselves, they gave money, arms and, above all, encouragement to two remarkable Shawnee Indian leaders who had a long-standing grudge against the United States.

The Shawnee had been forced westward from Ohio by the pressure of new settlers coming into the state, and now lived in the Indiana Territory. Their headquarters was a place they called The Prophet's Town, and it was there that their chief, Tecumseh, worked day and night on a scheme to drive American settlers from the entire West. Brilliant and dignified, Tecumseh was an accomplished orator who had enjoyed the advantages of a good education. He dreamed of establishing a confederation of all the Indian tribes from Canada to Florida.

According to his plan, they would unite under his leadership, and it was his secret aim to burn to the ground every American city, town, and village from the Great Lakes territories, down through the states of Kentucky and Tennessee to the Alabama and Mississippi territories on the Gulf of Mexico. Never before had anyone been able to unite all the tribes, but Tecumseh was a cunning, clever man.

Knowing that most warriors were superstitious, ignorant, and in awe of the supernatural, he gave his brother, who was his assistant, the name "The Prophet." The persuasive Tecumseh traveled constantly, and everywhere he preached the same doctrine. The Prophet, he said, was endowed with unique religious powers. He was able to communicate directly with the gods of the many tribes, the gods of sun and moon and stars, of the wind and rain, of the earth and sky. The gods, Tecumseh said, told the secrets of the future to The Prophet, who in turn confided in Tecumseh. This made the brothers invincible. Together, at the head of a mighty force, they would drive the American intruders out of their lands, the lands of their ancestors since time immemorial.

At first the followers of Tecumseh and The Prophet were limited to a small band of Shawnee. But gradually Tecumseh's influence and power spread. The Cherokee and Chickasaw of Tennessee came to believe in him. So did the Miami, who still lived in Ohio, and the Potawatamie of the Michigan Territory. The Illinois nation called him their savior, as did the Sauk and Fox of the Wisconsin area. Only the tribes of the Alabama and Mississippi Territories—the

Choctaw and Creek, Biloxi and Natchez and Pensacola—
were not yet under his spell.

Tecumseh was devoting the better part of 1811 to improving his relations with these Southern tribes. He visited
them often, carrying with him gifts of British money and
whiskey. The firearms they wanted would come later, after
they swore allegiance to him.

One American was responsible for keeping watch on Tecumseh and The Prophet, Governor William Henry Harrison of the Indiana Territory. A bluff, hearty man of thirty-
eight, Harrison was the product of an extraordinary back-
ground. His father, a signer of the Declaration of Independence, had served several terms as Governor of Virginia,
and William Henry had known all of America's greatest leaders—Washington and Jefferson and Patrick Henry, among
others—from earliest childhood.

Imbued with a fiery patriotism, he had obtained a commission in the Army and had served in the Western territories under an inspiring military leader who had been one
of the heroes of the Revolution, General Anthony Wayne.
Harrison had been promoted several times, and had re-
signed from the Army to become Governor of the vast
Territory. But he was still a soldier at heart, as well as a
statesman in practice.

For two years he had tried to negotiate with Tecumseh
and The Prophet. Both had lied to him repeatedly, pro-
fessing friendship for the United States. But Governor Harrison knew better. He had heard rumors of the confederation they were building, and his scouts brought him a steady
stream of reports on the money, arms, and ammunition the
British were giving them.

One day in late October, 1811, Harrison was eating a
dinner of buffalo steak with several of his aides at his
headquarters in the northeastern part of the Territory, Fort

Wayne. Protected by thick, double walls of heavy logs and warmed by a blazing fire, they ate quietly, saying little. Like all who had lived for any length of time on the frontier, they rarely spoke merely for the sake of conviviality. Certainly the burly Harrison was not one to encourage small talk, and the members of his staff kept their thoughts to themselves rather than risk his sardonic half-smile, which could make even the most courageous wince.

A sentry who belonged to one of the two companies of Regular Army troops under Harrison's command came into the dining room and saluted. "Sir," he said, "there's a half-breed from the Mishawaka tribe here to see you. I told him you're eating, but he claims it's urgent, and he wants to talk to you privately."

Everyone at Fort Wayne knew it was the Governor's policy to receive all visitors and, if they wished, to listen in private to anything they wanted to tell him. Friends who were concerned over his safety had warned him that it would be easy for a disgruntled brave to slip a knife between his ribs, but the Governor had insisted he could take care of himself.

Leaving half his meal untouched, he checked the pistols in his belt to make certain they were loaded, and as he rose he slipped a short, double-edged knife under the sleeve of his buckskin shirt.

The half-breed was waiting in a guard room just inside the log palisades of the fort. General Wayne had once decreed that suspicious visitors were not to be allowed beyond the outer perimeter of a fort because they might carry a mental blueprint of the place to a potential enemy. Harrison had kept the sensible rule in force.

The half-breed, a buffalo-hide cloak hanging from his shoulders, raised his left hand, palm held upward as a gesture of friendship. "Long-Jaw Williams greets his friend," he said, speaking in the language of the Illinois, which most tribes of the area used.

Harrison replied in the same tongue. "The sachem of the Rifle Men greets his friend." He relaxed, knowing that Long-Jaw Williams, for years one of his most reliable paid informants, could be trusted. But one thing puzzled him. If the Shawnee, Miami, or other tribes of the region had seen him coming to Fort Wayne, he would be regarded by all the Indians as a traitor. "Why does Long-Jaw come to this lodge?"

The man accepted a chair that the Governor offered him and, his face grave, drew a folded batch of somewhat tattered papers from a pouch at his waist. "Long-Jaw learned to read a little of the tongue of the Americans at the mission school. He knew his friend, the sachem, would want to see these."

Harrison glanced through the documents, and his temples pounded. He was holding a neatly written inventory of weapons recently delivered by the British to Tecumseh and his brother at The Prophet's Town. Each sheet carried the official seal of the Royal Army's adjutant general for Canada, and the Governor could not doubt the authenticity of the papers. In all, he saw, the savages had received more than fifteen hundred muskets and vast supplies of bullets and gunpowder. "How did Long-Jaw get these papers?" he wanted to know.

The half-breed explained that he and two fellow warriors of the Mishawaka, a small tribe living on the southeastern shores of Lake Michigan that had long been at odds with the Shawnee, had killed five Englishmen traveling north across the rolling prairie wilderness after delivering the arms to The Prophet's Town. As proof of the encounter, the half-breed pointed to two scalp-locks with blond hair hanging from his belt.

Harrison had lived on the frontier long enough to look at the grisly trophies without flinching.

Long-Jaw had two more nuggets of information to impart. Tecumseh, he said, was in the South to get recruits for a major uprising scheduled to begin in the early spring. In the meanwhile, warriors from all parts of Indiana, Illinois, and Michigan were already arriving at The Prophet's Town, eager to take part in the campaign.

The Governor gave his informant a new rifle, two knives, and twenty dollars in gold. Then, still clutching the captured British papers, he retired to his private quarters deep inside the fort to analyze the situation.

Now he had proof of what he had long believed, that the British were arming the Indians and urging them to fight the Americans. He knew, too, that his own difficulties would be compounded with each passing week between now and spring. The arrival of still more braves would make it increasingly hard for him to win a campaign against the savages. And the coming of winter, always bitterly cold in the prairie country, would hamper his operations.

He was tempted to strike the Indians at once, before heavy snow fell. However, he was uncertain whether he had the authority to act on his own initiative, as he was expected to obtain permission for major military moves from the Secretary of War. On the other hand, he was afraid long weeks would pass before a courier could travel to Washington City, obtain a ruling from the government, and return to Fort Wayne.

Government regulations were strict, Harrison realized, and he was supposed to obey them. All the same . . . the temptation to take matters in his own hands was almost overwhelming. He began to pace up and down his narrow, simply furnished office, the heels of his boots striking hard on the plain pine boards of the floor.

The knowledge that Tecumseh was hundreds of miles

from The Prophet's Town helped the Governor make up his mind. If there were a battle now, the Indians would be forced to do without the services of their most effective leader. Scores—perhaps hundreds—of lives would be saved.

Harrison made his decision and, once he had settled the issue, banished the question from his mind. He stood for a long time before a map of the Territory pinned to the rough log wall, then summoned his two immediate subordinates, one a colonel and the other a lieutenant colonel.

They listened with the impassive gravity of frontiersmen as he described the situation to them, but the light in their eyes said far more than mere words.

"How many militiamen can you muster in ten days?" Harrison asked.

The colonel thought for a few moments. "With luck, about one thousand. Most farmers have already taken in their autumn harvest crops."

The Governor nodded. "We'll be outnumbered by at least one and one-half to one. So we'll need the element of surprise to tip the scales in our favor." He turned to the lieutenant colonel. "Arrange for the militia companies to gather at fifteen or twenty mustering points. I want them to leave their homes quietly with their firearms and a two-week food supply in their blanket-rolls. I want no parades through towns and villages, and no speech-making anywhere. Don't tell anyone our real intentions, not even the battalion and company commanders. If necessary, let the militia think they've been called out on an exercise of some sort."

The lieutenant colonel smiled wryly. "They'll know you haven't called them out at this time of year for their health, Governor," he said. "But I'll do my best."

"The element of surprise is essential," Harrison replied firmly. "A defeat would be ruinous, and we can't hope to win unless we catch the savages completely off guard.

Luckily, they don't know we've learned their intentions. They're spending their days in The Prophet's Town boasting how they'll scalp settlers by the thousands next April or May. They mustn't learn of our mobilization, even by accident."

"There will be no accidents, sir," the lieutenant colonel assured him grimly.

When William Henry Harrison trusted someone, he gave the man full responsibility for his task. Nodding, he said, "That will be all for the present, gentlemen. I'll ask you to meet me again in three days to help plan our tactics. And I suggest you spend your spare time practicing your marksmanship, as I intend to do. Even senior officers will have to make every bullet count!"

The militiamen, nearly one thousand strong, met at the mustering points in various parts of the Indiana Territory and then made their way as unobtrusively as possible to the grand rendezvous, a forest of towering beech and graceful sycamore trees near the Wabash River. There the Governor was waiting for them with his staff and the two companies of Regular Army troops.

No force had ever looked less warlike. No one was wearing a uniform, and even the Regulars were dressed in faded buckskin shirts and trousers that blended with the gray-brown of the autumn landscape. Full security precautions were observed; the men were not allowed to smoke their pipes, and no cooking fires were lighted. The troops made no complaint and ate jerked beef and parched corn, washed down with river water.

The last of the men expected arrived at the bivouac late on the afternoon of November 6, 1811, and shortly after sundown Governor Harrison called a meeting of his little corps. He hated speech-making, but had never forgotten a lesson General Wayne had taught him: Americans always fought better when they were told a battle plan and knew why they were fighting.

Harrison confined himself to a few brief remarks. A failure now, he explained, would almost certainly guarantee that thousands of settlers, including women and children, would be killed by the savages the following year. He made no attempt to arouse the troops but quietly said he expected every man to do his duty.

The tactics he had devised were simple. The Prophet's Town stood on the banks of the Tippecanoe River, and the corps would be divided into three main groups, which would surround the Indian settlement on all sides but that overlooking the river. The units on the flanks would be protected by woods and would be able to approach within a few hundred yards of the town. They would take their places first, and then the troops in the center, bolstered by the Regulars, would advance across open ground. No one was surprised when the Governor gave himself the most dangerous command, that of the center.

The march began at midnight. A cold, driving rain slowed the corps' progress only slightly, and officers moved up and down the line constantly, making sure that rifles and gunpowder were being protected. At four o'clock in the morning the Governor called a halt for a short, final rest and a hasty meal of more parched corn and jerked beef.

Harrison paid a quick visit to each unit, joked with the men in quiet tones, and let them see that his own calm appeared monumental. Not even the officers who knew him best guessed that he was suffering from severe tension. He was responsible for the unorthodox move; the lives of one thousand fellow Americans were in his keeping, and if his mission failed, the confederation of Tecumseh would become a reality and the whole frontier would soon be in flames. As for himself, his personal career would be destroyed. Neither the President nor the American people could permit him to remain in high public office if, after acting so completely on his own initiative, he did not win a victory.

The march was resumed, and the Governor, trudging at the head of the column behind his scouts, breathed a sigh of relief when the rain gradually stopped. The morning was bitterly cold, numbing the men's hands and feet, and a film of ice formed on the dead leaves and small branches of the trees. But the corps was drawing close to its goal now, and no one paid much heed to the weather.

At last, through the screen of trees, the vanguard saw The Prophet's Town directly ahead. Unlike many Indian communities, it had a permanent appearance. At least twenty long houses were built around a rectangular-shaped open space in the center of the town. Each of these structures, looking solid and strong in the half-light of dawn, was large enough to accommodate pallets for one hundred warriors. In these long houses slept the warriors of many nations who hoped to drive the Americans from the West.

The smaller houses, occupied by the Shawnee who were permanent residents of the town, were also made of wood, with animal skins stretched across their door-openings. Each was large enough to accommodate a whole family. On a slight hill dominating their immediate area were two larger houses of about the same size, and it was easy to guess that one was the home of Tecumseh, the other the dwelling of The Prophet.

Harrison took his large gold watch, which he had inherited from his father, out of his fob pocket and, resting the butt of his rifle on the ground, squinted at the dial in the early morning light. The columns forming the two flanks moved off silently to the right and the left, and he was giving them precisely a quarter of an hour to get into place.

As he waited, the Indian town began to stir. Smoke curled up into the cold morning air from three fires in the rectangular open space, and the Governor imagined that sqaws were at work preparing breakfast for the community. A dog barked somewhere inside the town, but no one paid any attention to the sound, and Harrison was relieved. Miraculously, the savages had not yet discovered the presence of their enemies, and the Governor prayed that his luck would remain good. The Indian sentries, expecting no attack, were being careless.

The time passed slowly, each minute a torture of suspense. The Regulars and militiamen crouching in the damp forest behind the Governor checked their rifles for the last time—and waited. The officers estimated the distance across the open prairie from the edge of the screen of trees to the town—and waited. Harrison curbed his own mounting impatience—and waited.

Then, suddenly, the blood-chilling sound of a war cry emanating from the forest on the left flank broke the silence. It was followed an instant later by a shot, and it was impossible to tell whether it had been made by a militiaman's rifle or an Indian sentry's musket.

In any event, the damage was done, and the men in The Prophet's Town were alerted to their danger. Warriors appeared, almost as though by magic, from the long houses, and Governor Harrison knew he could not wait the last five minutes for the units on the flanks to move into position. Whether they were ready or not, it was imperative that the troops in the center start at once across the exposed open space.

"Sound the charge," he ordered the bugler, and the piercing musical notes notified the commanders of the flanking units that the attack was under way.

The two companies of Regulars moved into the open

first, with Harrison insisting on leading them. Spread out across the tall, knee-high dead grass of the prairie, the men crouched low, their rifles ready for immediate use. Behind them, in a second wave, came the more cautious militia, the citizen-soldiers carefully following the example set for them by the professional fighting men.

A howling mob of warriors poured out into the prairie from the town, the angry savages indifferent to their own safety.

Harrison was quick to take advantage of the situation. "Pass the word," he called over his shoulder to the company commanders. "Fire at will!"

The men responded at once, and rifles began to crackle. But the savages had no intention of handing their foes a cheap or easy victory. Recovering their balance, they spread out in the high grass in front of the town and began to give as good as they received. The exchange of fire was spirited, and both sides were unable to advance.

Harrison's center was forced to take the brunt of the fighting for some minutes. The Indians, heavily outnumbering his force, applied such heavy pressure he was afraid he would have to fall back into the forest. Then the units on his right flank reached their assigned position and opened a brisk fire, too.

The savages were prepared for the maneuver, however, and already had men in place to meet this new assault. The pressure on the center was not alleviated until the troops on the left flank finally managed to struggle through the forest into position. Then, at last, Harrison's careful planning began to pay dividends, and his men had their opponents in a vise which they tightened little by little.

The warriors demonstrated great courage, and obviously had no intention of abandoning their town without a struggle to the death. The battle raged through the better part of the morning, and Harrison constantly moved troops from one sector to another, bolstering lines that weakened and applying added strength when one or another unit managed to gain ground.

Had Tecumseh been present, the eventual outcome of the battle might have been different. But his warriors, who owed their basic allegiance to many different tribes, slowly lost heart. And superior American leadership was the decisive factor. Harrison, his staff, and the commanders of militia companies knew what needed to be done, remained level-headed, and continued to set examples for their men.

The Indian women and children had been evacuated from The Prophet's Town during the morning, and the braves fell back into the community, fighting from house to house. Governor Harrison applied their own tactics against them, and a whole company of militia went to work making flaming firebrands and hurling them onto the roofs of long houses and smaller buildings.

Early in the afternoon, just as a watery sun broke through the clouds, the warriors decided they'd taken enough battering. The Illinois and the Miami slipped away and with difficulty made their way across the swollen Tippecanoe River. Others joined them, and in a matter of moments the better part of the savage army quit the field, fleeing in panic.

The Shawnee held out longer than any of their allies, but they knew they would be slaughtered if captured, and finally they fled, too, the remnants of their force scattering in the forest.

William Henry Harrison was master of the field and had smashed Tecumseh's British-inspired dream of forming a vast Indian confederation. Although neither Governor Harrison nor his subordinates realized it at the time, their triumph on November 7, 1811, actually marked the beginning of the War of 1812.

That night the weary troops rejoiced. But many long, weary years would pass before the United States would win another major victory on land.

CHAPTER SEVEN

Relations between the United States and Great Britain continued to deteriorate in the early months of 1812. American merchant seamen were still being impressed into the British Navy, and English gold, guns, and ammunition enabled the Indians to keep the West inflamed. Congress clamored for war, and President Madison at last decided that it was impossible to solve the dispute between the two nations by peaceful means.

All American ships, merchantmen as well as Navy vessels, were ordered to proceed to their home ports in April. No one wanted the still-superior Royal Navy to seize American ships on the high seas when hostilities actually began. Captains were given cannon, crews were trained in gunnery, and plans were made to provide protection for civilians when they left port again.

On June 1st, President Madison sent a solemn message to Congress. In it he outlined the causes of a breakdown in Anglo-American relations. Great Britain, he declared, refused to respect American rights as a neutral nation. Impressments continued. British warships hovered off the coast of the United States and seized outbound merchant ships. And the British were inciting the Indians of the West.

"It is difficult," he said bluntly, "to account for the activity and combinations which have been for some time developing themselves among tribes in constant intercourse

with British traders and garrisons, without connecting their
hostility with that influence.

"We behold, on the side of Great Britain, a state of war
against the United States, and on the side of the United
States, a state of peace toward Great Britain."

Congress, he declared, had to face a stern choice, that of
deciding whether the United States "should remain pas-
sive" or should "oppose force to force in defense of our
natural rights."

The issue was debated in both the Senate and the House
of Representatives for more than two weeks, but the issue
was never in serious doubt. On June 18, 1812, Congress
declared war against Great Britain by an overwhelming
vote. Once again a struggling young country took up arms
against the most powerful nation on earth.

Canada appeared defenseless, and Henry Clay, now
Speaker of the House, said publicly, "Kentucky riflemen can
capture Quebec and Montreal without help."

Even former President Jefferson, usually so cautious,
wrote from his home at Monticello, Virginia, "In order that
our forces take the major cities of Canada is no more than
a matter of marching."

Madison's reelection as President later in the year was
assured, and he promised to take personal charge of all war
activities.

But clouds quickly appeared on the horizon. Major General Henry Lee, known to all Americans as "Light-Horse
Harry" and a great cavalry hero of the Revolution, was the
man best suited to take command of the American armies
in the field but was too ill to serve. A strong anti-war feeling
continued to exist in New England, and militia units from
that part of the country were unable to obtain enough volunteers to fill their ranks.

The British, long experienced in the grim art of war,
quickly transferred a large number of troops to the New

World, swiftly transporting them from England to Halifax. American imports had sagged through the years of blockade-induced depression, and Secretary of the Treasury Albert Gallatin was unable to raise enough money in taxes to prosecute the vigorous, aggressive war that the United States would have to wage if she hoped to achieve a decisive victory.

The generals selected for active command had held junior commands during the Revolution. They were inexperienced in dealing with large armies, and most were elderly, ranging in age from fifty-five to seventy years. Henry Dearborn was an administrator; Harrison—the Tippecanoe conqueror—understood Indian fighting but had never faced real troops in battle; Thomas Pinckney had enjoyed a somewhat less than distinguished career in Washington's Continentals during the Revolution; and William Hull, who was given the key command post in the West at Fort Detroit, was an exceptionally cautious man.

Nevertheless, the people expected quick victories from the Army and hoped the Navy would perform miracles. Certainly there was some basis for the optimism that the whole country felt when weighing the Navy's prospects. Her officers and men were hard-bitten and experienced, and had learned their profession in the wars with the Barbary states of North Africa. The new frigates and sloops were solid ships. And the Navy's gunnery was superb.

"Ordinarily," said Captain William Bainbridge, soon to be promoted to the rank of commodore, "a frigate of forty to fifty guns can't be expected to hold her own against a huge ship-of-the-line that has at least seventy-four guns. Well, we have frigates, but no ships-of-the-line. So our gunnery *must* be better than the enemy's if we're to equalize the odds."

Commodore Isaac Hull, commander of the *Constitution,* a frigate, and the senior officer on sea duty, expressed himself modestly at a dinner given in his honor at a restaurant in New York City. "Don't light any victory bonfires yet," he told the cheering civilians. "My colleagues and I know that the Royal Navy is the strongest force on the seas. We'll do our best, but don't expect a young barracuda to devour a cunning, full-grown shark with very sharp teeth."

Other naval commanders, among them Stephen Decatur and James Barron, made no comments at all. Instead they kept the crews of their frigates hard at work improving their marksmanship. "I won't be satisfied," Decatur wrote to Bainbridge, his former superior, "until our lads can use cannon as expertly as a Tennessee frontiersman uses his long rifle."

The Army made plans for the invasion of Canada, and it was agreed that there would be a two-pronged offensive, with Dearborn moving against Quebec in the East and Hull striking from Fort Detroit in the west. Newspapers freely discussed the strategy, and Secretary Monroe complained bitterly to the President.

"We're advertising," he said. "We're giving free information to the enemy. We must learn, and quickly, to act first and talk later."

The declaration of war was greeted with wild enthusiasm in the Western states and territories, and nowhere did the flame of patriotic fervor burn higher than in Nashville. Many farmers and artisans volunteered for the state's militia even though there wasn't enough ammunition on hand to form more than one division.

Perhaps the Westerner most eager to join the colors was a Nashville politician and planter, lawyer and former judge. But the Regular Army could not take the demands of Andrew Jackson seriously. He was middle-aged, and although he had fought the Cherokee as a young pioneer newly arrived in Tennessee many years earlier, he had no authentic qualifications as a soldier. His rank as a brigadier general of state militia was a political reward, nothing more, and senior clerks in the War Department deliberately "lost" his application for a Federal appointment.

The fuming, disappointed Jackson was forced to stay at home and read glowing newspaper accounts of the victories that other American generals intended to win. "By the Eternal!" he told the friends who came to visit him at his home, The Hermitage, "Canada is going to be a tougher nut to crack than any of these foolish optimists realize. And while the generals are patting each other on the back, the Indian tribes of the frontier are stirring. We're going to have trouble—plenty of trouble—closer to home than Canada. May the Almighty help us if the Creek and Choctaw go on the warpath. I'll try to be patient. I'll wait for a spell. But if they don't grant me a commission reasonably soon, I'll round up some boys who know how to shoot and see what we can do on our own!"

Commodore Isaac Hull was unhappy, too. He planned to sail from New York on July 12th to seek out the enemy, and the newspapers of the city carried accounts of the *Constitution's* impending departure on their front pages. "I wonder if they realize," he told his subordinates on the night before the frigate left port, "that the town is undoubtedly riddled with enemy spies. I'm willing to wager—at heavy odds—that the British know what we're about and will be scouring the Atlantic for us."

For ninety-six hours his fears appeared groundless, but on the fifth day out of port Hull's gloomy prophecy was suddenly realized.

"Sail ho!" the lookout in the crow's nest shouted. "Sir, there's a squadron bearing down on us."

Hull, although thirty-nine years old, climbed high into the rigging of the *Constitution* to see the approaching squadron himself. He studied the vessels through his glass, and his heart sank. Two frigates, each as strong as the *Con-*

stitution, were shepherding a mammoth flagship, a mighty ship-of-the-line capable of blowing him out of the water. He saw at least three small sloops of war, too, the "eyes" of the squadron, almost incredibly swift little vessels capable of keeping a close watch on any ship trying to escape.

Such escape, Hull knew, was imperative. No distinguishing pennants had yet been hoisted, but he was positive the squadron was a unit of the Royal Navy assigned to the duty of blockading the American coast. He was equally certain that the admiral or commodore in command had been given the specific task of seeking, finding, and destroying him.

"Tack to starboard," he called as he descended to the deck. "Crowd on every ounce of sail we can carry!"

The flight of the *Constitution* from an infinitely superior foe had begun.

For more than a quarter of a century after that encounter, officers and men who had sailed on the voyage boasted that they had served with Isaac Hull. Rarely—if ever—in the long history of sea warfare had the sailors of any nation taken part in such an incredible adventure.

The British pursued their quarry with the bulldog determination for which they were justly famous, but the *Constitution,* almost a living, breathing thing under Hull's sensitive touch, played a deadly game of hide-and-seek with her foes. One moment she was a ghost-ship, a wraith that disappeared into nowhere. Then she became a sleek racer, miraculously endowed with the ability to out-run the fastest sloops.

Hull's seamanship was superior to that of the world's most experienced sailors, and for three days and nights he maneuvered ceaselessly as he eluded the Royal Navy squadron. For three days and nights he remained on his quarter-deck, sleepless yet needing no sleep, exhausted yet endowed with boundless energy.

Shortly before dusk on the third evening of the chase, a

dense fog settled over the western reaches of the Atlantic, the wind died away, and Hull was at last forced to give up his flight. His sails had become useless, and he reluctantly admitted to his officers that it would be senseless to continue until the weather cleared and a fresh breeze sprang up.

The weary officers were relieved. They told each other that even though they were fog-bound, so were the British. For the moment, at least, the *Constitution* was safe.

But Commodore Hull preferred to take no chances and restlessly paced his quarterdeck. The chances that the enemy could find him in the fog were remote, but he was a man who believed in reducing every risk to the minimum. While he debated with himself, wondering what to do next, he suddenly heard the sounds of human voices drifting across the water and stopped short.

Incredible though it seemed, the British squadron had cast anchor only a quarter of a mile off his port stern. Whenever the fog cleared away he would be within easy range of the great cannon mounted by the Royal Navy ship-of-the-line and frigates. At any moment the weather might improve, and within a few minutes thereafter the *Constitution* could be sent to the bottom.

Hull's mind worked furiously, and after notifying his officers and crew that he wanted them to maintain utter silence and show no lights, he evolved a remarkable escape plan.

Two longboats were quietly lowered into the sea, rags and other pieces of cloth muffling their oarlocks. Forty husky sailors were seated in each longboat, and on them depended the life or death of the Yankee frigate.

Stout lines were stretched from the *Constitution* to the two boats. The eighty sailors began to row in unison, straining at the oars yet daring to make no sound as their blades cut through the water. Slowly the American warship inched

away from her pursuers, the gap between them lengthen-
ing to a half-mile, three-quarters of a mile, finally a mile.

Night had descended, and the combination of fog and
dark made it impossible for a man to see his hand in front
of his face. Nevertheless, Hull would have directed the tired
oarsmen to continue, but a new complication unexpectedly
developed. The sea was running more swiftly now, and the
sailors in the two boats were scarcely able to hold their
own in the swells. Unless something drastic was done, the
Constitution would either have to drop her heaviest anchor
—and risk a delay in moving on again when the weather
improved—or might drift back in the direction from which
she had just come.

Isaac Hull was equal to this new emergency. Summoning
his senior lieutenants to the quarterdeck, he told them in a
soft murmur, "Gentlemen, we've got to put still more distance between us and that squadron. We're going to kedge."

They thought him mad, but had to accept his order.

Under the best of circumstances, kedging was a difficult
and tricky operation. In mid-Atlantic at night, in a heavy
fog, and with a powerful enemy squadron no more than a
mile away, the very idea seemed insane.

But Commodore Hull had his way. A longboat returned
to the *Constitution* for an anchor, then moved away again,
trailing lines spliced together to make a single line some
hundreds of yards long. When the line became taut, the
anchor was dropped, and the men in the longboat began the
fantastically tiring task of hauling in the line hand-over-
hand.

Now the great frigate literally moved only a few inches
at a time. But she responded to the steady pressure on the
line and at last reached the longboat. Then the anchor was
hauled up and transferred to the other boat, and the whole
laborious process was repeated. Little by little through the

long hours of the foggy night, the *Constitution* continued to edge away from her adversaries.

As members of the boat crews tired, they were replaced by others. The kedging operation went on—and on. Through the whole back-breaking process, no man spoke aloud. Each time the anchor was lowered, it was eased gently into the sea, never dropped. Living ghosts, through almost super-human toil and ingenuity, were leading a ghost-ship to safety.

At four o'clock in the morning, after more than eight hours of unceasing labor, Commodore Hull knew that his men had reached the limits of their endurance. The kedging operation was halted, the frigate anchored in the open sea, and the men went off for a brief rest.

But Isaac Hull refused to sit, much less go to bed for even an hour. He knew that at daybreak the chances were good that the weather would change. And when the first streaks of dawn appeared in the sky, his vigil was rewarded. A faint breeze began to stir.

All hands were called on deck. The sailing division was sent aloft, and the ship's sails were spread to catch the wind. The anchor was weighed, and Hull was on the move again as the fog finally cleared. He attained such a good start that, by the time the sun rose in a cloudless sky, the British squadron had vanished somewhere over the horizon.

The *Constitution* returned to port, and all America hailed her epic voyage. Isaac Hull was hailed as a sailor without peer, and congressmen sang his praises in speech after speech. But the grizzled Commodore was a thoroughly un-happy man. Praise meant nothing to him, and no matter what Congress and the press said, he felt he had accom-plished nothing positive.

It was true that he had demonstrated superb seamanship in his escape, but the purpose of fighting men in war was to destroy the enemy's ability to wage war. Hull yearned to prove that he could do more than run away.

Orders sending the *Constitution* to sea again were delayed in Washington City, where clerks accustomed to a leisurely peacetime pace were unable to keep up with the new demands being made on them. Hull wrote a letter, asking that he be allowed to proceed immediately. There was no reply, and he wrote a second time, allowing three days for approval.

When it did not come in time to meet his self-imposed deadline, he lost patience and put to sea again without orders. He and his crew were seeking vengeance—and found it when the *Constitution* sighted a British frigate of approximately her own size, sailing alone. She was the *Guerrière*, and her captain demonstrated that he, too, was eager for a fight.

In the furious battle that followed, the long hours that American gunnery crews had spent in the drudgery of practice paid handsome dividends. The *Guerrière* was forced to strike her colors, and Hull brought her back to the United States a captive.

Now America really went wild with joy. Commodore Hull received a gold medal from a grateful Congress, and the *Constitution*, which had suffered remarkably little damage in the battle, was given the affectionate nickname "Old Ironsides" by a happy public.

But the celebration was short-lived. While Hull was winning glory and a victory at sea, the field commanders of the Army were inadvertently setting the stage for a tragedy of far-reaching consequences. Dearborn, the senior major general, was scheduled to move north into Canada via Lake Champlain and take Montreal. Generals Alexander Smyth and Stephen Van Rensselaer were to move into Canada via Niagara, and William Hull, stationed at Fort Detroit, was to occupy the Great Lakes region of Canada. On paper, the plan looked good.

The execution of the scheme was another matter. Dearborn spent long, anxious days conferring with his own subordinates and the Navy officers who would transport his corps up Lake Champlain. He wanted nothing to go wrong, and in his caution he waited too long. By the time he was finally ready, the British had been able to move a strong force from Halifax to Quebec and Montreal.

Dearborn's untried troops, most of them raw militiamen, committed a near-mutiny and refused to cross the border into Canada. Smyth's troops were Regulars, willing to follow wherever he led them, but Van Rensselaer's New York militiamen got very cold feet when they learned that Dearborn's column had stalled its own drive.

Hull, in the meantime, had started to carry out his part of the assignment and had moved confidently into Canada, the British forces of General Isaac Brock retreating before his advancing corps. Then Hull received word that his fellow commanders had not yet acted. He was isolated, in danger of being cut off, and immediately retreated to Fort Detroit.

Whether this sudden act was prudent or foolish was debated for years. Regardless of its wisdom or stupidity, Brock was quick to take advantage of the situation. Reinforced by large numbers of Ottawa and other savages, the British moved in for the kill.

There were women and children at Fort Detroit, and the Indians were thirsting for scalps. Hull, who had demonstrated his own personal courage in the Revolution, feared for the safety of the non-combatants. Brock's troops were vastly outnumbered by his savage allies, and Hull was afraid the women and children would be killed if he allowed a battle to take place.

While he pondered his terrible dilemma, Commodore Hull arrived in the United States with the *Constitution* leading its prize of war. The New York *Gazette*, one of the nation's leading newspapers, crowed, "August 2nd, the day of the *Constitution's* triumph, will live forever in our history."

Precisely two weeks later, on August 16th, the Commodore's unfortunate namesake had to make the most difficult decision of his life. Fort Detroit was surrounded by swarms of shrieking savages. It was easy to see from the watch-towers that General Brock's own British force was a small one.

General Hull surrendered to his opponent without firing a shot, on condition that the women and children be allowed to depart in safety.

The news of his capitulation stunned the country. All thoughts of an invasion of Canada had to be abandoned, and with them went the fond hopes of winning the war quickly. President Madison and his advisers took stock of the new situation, but one didn't have to be a member of the Cabinet to realize that the British occupation of Fort Detroit placed the entire West in danger.

An apprehensive shiver shot through the Michigan, Indiana, and Illinois Territories. The Cherokee, most powerful of the Southern Indian nations, took heart at the unexpected development and became restive. Raids in southern Tennessee and western Kentucky were a sign that there would be worse to come.

The entire nation demanded that someone be punished for the Army's shameful collapse. Perhaps it could have been argued that Dearborn and Van Rensselaer were at least partly to blame. But General Hull was the obvious object of the country's wrath. He was tried by a court-martial, which convicted him on a charge of cowardice. President Madison, moved to compassion, pardoned him because of his faultless previous record.

Neither the trial nor the pardon altered the basic military situation. The United States, which had gone to war with such high hopes, was now in mortal danger of being invaded—and defeated. Great Britain had learned that American generals were incompetent and American militiamen mere raw recruits unfit for use in battle. The War Office in London made its own plans accordingly.

CHAPTER EIGHT

The second year of the war found the United States floundering. In spite of the gallant efforts made by the American Navy, British warships continued to blockade the seacoast from Maine to the Spanish Floridas. International trade was reduced to an even smaller trickle, and Treasury Department tax receipts continued to dwindle. "I hope," President Madison confided to his Cabinet, "that we'll have enough income to pay the wages of the militia troops we're calling to duty."

The atmosphere in the nation's capital was gloomy. "We are literally borne down," said John C. Calhoun, "under the effects of errors and mismanagement."

The all-important military future remained dim. A new Secretary of War, John Armstrong, unimaginatively proposed that the plan to invade Canada be revived. Neither generals nor civilians could think of a better scheme, so his suggestion was adopted. Unfortunately, Armstrong and his associates were daydreaming, and no one knew it better than William Henry Harrison, now a major general.

Harrison had been given command in the West, and tried valiantly but in vain to deal with problems too great for him. Regular Army troops placed under his command refused to respect someone they considered a mere Indian fighter, raw militia units were helpless in combat against

British veterans, and the senior American officers quarreled among themselves.

Slowly the British moved southward through Michigan and Indiana, pushing the Americans before them until, finally, Harrison was able to establish a fairly stable defense line on the Wabash River. Then the enemy edged eastward into Ohio. The citizens of that young state became wildly alarmed, thousands joined the militia, and the British advance was halted. This accomplishment could scarcely be called a victory, as Redcoats were still controlling tens of thousands of square miles of American territory.

General Harrison was proving more reliable than some of his predecessors but was no firebrand capable of winning the devotion of his men and inspiring them to perform great deeds. "We need a new George Washington," Henry Clay told the President.

Finding such a leader seemed an insoluble problem. Grundy and other Tennesseeans sang the praises of their friend Andrew Jackson and managed to arouse a mild interest in him at the War Department. But Jackson, still chafing because he had no part in the war, impetuously allowed himself to be drawn into a duel after a personal argument. He was so seriously wounded that he was lucky to escape with his life, and temporarily lost the use of one arm.

General James Wilkinson, who had acquired a reputation for bravery during the Revolution, took Dearborn's place but proved equally ineffective. Only one young general in the entire sector, Winfield Scott, was demonstrating an ability to plan campaigns and win battles, but his victories over small British and Indian corps were minor and did not influence the overall conduct of the war.

Political disputes continued to divide and weaken the United States, too. John Quincy Adams of Massachusetts, son of the nation's second President and himself destined to become the country's Chief Executive, ably summed up the attitude found in his part of the land. "New England's voice has long been dominant in our affairs," he said. "Our merchants and manufacturers and shipowners have been influential since the first days of the Republic. Rightly or wrongly, they are afraid that, if they win the war, the creation of many new states in the West will force them to play a minor role in the nation's future development. So their support of the government is half-hearted."

"Perhaps a few resounding victories will persuade New England to march in step with the rest of the country," President Madison said to his Secretary of State.

James Monroe's response was cynical. "A British invasion of New England might be even more effective. The younger men there don't remember the Redcoat occupation of Boston in the early days of the Revolution."

Only the British need to use every available soldier in their long struggle with Napoleon, now reaching its climax, prevented London from sending an overwhelming force to the New World. The United States continued to live on borrowed time.

Then, in the summer of 1813, an incident occurred in the Alabama Territory that was to change the entire course of the conflict in ways that no one could have had the foresight to predict.

Fort Mims was a small American outpost on the Alabama River, located deep in the Creek Indian country. It was a typical fort, consisting of four blockhouses, each located at a corner of a rectangular palisade of thick logs. In the compound were a number of cabins where the families of militiamen lived.

The settlers accepted duty there philosophically. A man was required to spend only ninety days in service, the cabins were comfortable, and wives and children enjoyed the quiet, lazy days. The youngsters swam and fished in the river, the older boys often went hunting in the forest, and the men themselves never fired a rifle in anger.

There had been a flurry of excitement two years earlier, to be sure. At that time, Tecumseh—who had now been made a brigadier general by the British—had visited the Creek. But his attempt to persuade them to join his confederation of Indian nations had failed—or so the settlers believed. They had no way of knowing that the half-breed leader of the Creek, William Weatherford, was merely biding his time. Weatherford wanted to satisfy himself that the United States was truly losing the war before he cast in his lot with its enemies.

By the late summer of 1813 he was convinced that America was incapable of winning the war. The invasion of Canada was still a vague dream, the British blockade of Yankee ports had virtually ruined American industry, and agents from Montreal and Quebec appeared regularly in the Territory, bringing the Indians gifts of arms, ammunition, money, and liquor.

Weatherford decided to strike his first blow at Fort Mims. The garrison there consisted of seventy militiamen commanded by Major Daniel Beasley. In all, there were approximately two hundred and fifty persons in the place, including the wives and children of the part-time soldiers. Samuel Mims, a wealthy planter of the area, on whose property the fort was located, also happened to be there with his wife and two daughters.

The Creek had been so quiet all summer that Major Beasley had been lulled into a false sense of security. His own military service had been limited, and, like his men, he was thoroughly bored. Although he undoubtedly knew he should maintain a sentry watch twenty-four hours a day, he and his troops had seen no sign of Creek braves in the eighty days they had been on duty. Furthermore, they had no reason to suspect trouble.

Whether the guards were asleep at their posts in the towers on the night of August 30, 1813, or whether they hadn't bothered to mount sentry duty is a mystery that has never been solved. Asleep or awake, absent or present, the militiamen were careless.

Weatherford and a band of more than five hundred warriors approached the fort from the south sometime around midnight. Moving stealthily, they surrounded the rectangular palisade and crept forward. Their leader soon discovered that his precautions were unnecessary. Even though some of his men approaching the walls on the west side had to cross open ground, where trees had been cleared away the previous spring, no alarm was given and no shots were fired.

The savages, scarcely able to believe their good fortune, climbed over the palisade and opened the gate for their comrades. The horde swarmed in.

What happened in the nightmare that followed was later deduced by other militiamen who surveyed the grisly scene. Every inhabitant of Fort Mims, without exception, was killed and scalped. Mothers and their children were slaughtered in their beds. A few of the militiamen awoke in time to see what was happening and tried to put up a fight, but it was too late. Badly outnumbered, they had no chance to reach for their rifles. Knives and tomahawks rendered them helpless, and they were dispatched by muskets.

The butchery lasted no more than a few minutes. Weatherford wanted to leave, but his blood-crazed men insisted on looting the fort. They took weapons and clothing, cooking utensils and furniture—virtually everything they could carry away with them. Only at Weatherford's insistence did they refrain from burning the whole compound to the ground. The chief knew, even if his subordinates did not, that there would be strong repercussions, and he wanted the bodies left intact so they could be buried.

When the news of the Fort Mims massacre spread, the entire United States was stunned, then infuriated. No one was angrier than the convalescing Andrew Jackson, who had finally obtained his commission as a major general, but was too ill to leave his bed. Nevertheless, he displayed a stubborn determination of a kind shown by no other soldier in the American Army since the start of the war.

"The health of your General is restored," he wrote to his Tennessee militia. "He will command an expedition in person to teach the Creek a lesson and make the frontier safe for all who have settled there."

His physicians, supported by Mrs. Jackson, told him he would harm himself if he failed to rest at home for at least another six to eight weeks. If he went into the field, they said, he might kill himself. What was more, he would have to carry his left arm in a sling for several months.

Andrew Jackson heard all they had to say but continued to think of Fort Mims—and the thousands of settlers now jeopardized by the rampaging warriors of the Creek nation.

"I'm going to march," he said, "in nine days. And no power on this earth is strong enough to stop me!"

Billy Blakesly, cabin boy of the brig *Marilyn*, stood on the main deck of the four-hundred-and-fifty-ton merchantman, staring in the dark across the vast expanse of black sea. The night was warm, but Billy shivered, willingly admitting to himself that he was frightened. At fourteen, after two years at sea, he supposed he should be immune to fear, but the *Marilyn's* luck had been good too long.

She had returned safely to Boston from ten voyages, slipping through the British blockade each time. It was miraculous that the *Marilyn* had been spared when so many other ships had been captured or sunk. Billy had no idea what had become of his uncle, the mate on another brig, or to his two cousins, crew members of still another. Americans put out to sea from the United States—and then vanished. It made a boy nervous when he tried to guess their fate. And it wasn't much consolation to tell himself that the British were no longer forcing Americans to serve in the Royal Navy. Other, far worse, things were done to wartime enemies.

But the possibility of death at sea or that of falling into the hands of the British were, in a sense, the least of Billy's concerns. The *Marilyn's* cargo was desperately needed by a nation unable to obtain a variety of manufactured goods essential in a civilized land. One crate in the aft hold contained surgical instruments that members of the rapidly expanding medical profession had been demanding. Unless the brig ran the enemy blockade safely, surgeons from Boston to Baltimore would go empty-handed.

In the forward hold were small complicated machines, tiny but efficient, each of them necessary in the manufacture of high-quality cloth. The United States had to expand her textile factories now that she could no longer obtain woolen and cotton bolts from England, and in order to make such cloth the owners of factories needed machinery that no one in America had the facilities or technical knowledge to create.

Maybe it was foolish to believe that the outcome of the war depended on the *Marilyn's* ability to outwit the foes trying to prevent her from reaching port. But Billy knew that until the United States Navy was strong enough to protect the country's merchantmen each brig that slipped through the hands of the British won a substantial victory. These triumphs were rarely mentioned in the newspapers, and Congress awarded no gold medals to the masters of merchant vessels. But the sturdy little ships were providing the United States with lifeblood, the equipment the nation required to transform her from an agricultural to a manufacturing country. Everyone knew she could no longer rely on Europe for her manufactured goods, but had to depend on herself. So the cargo of the *Marilyn*—and of scores of merchantmen like her—was worth more than the gold and jewels of the Indies.

In the distance Billy could see two tiny pinpoints of light. His sense of excitement mounting, he realized they were the twin oil lamps that burned high in the tower on Beacon Hill as a guide to seafarers. The *Marilyn* was nearing home.

Far off the brig's starboard bow two long, sleek ships suddenly loomed up out of the dark, however, and the boy's heart sank. A pair of powerful British frigates was bearing down on the slow-moving merchantman.

The master of the *Marilyn* was thoroughly aware of his danger and, crowding on all the sail he could carry, raced the enemy toward Boston Harbor. The brig, which seemed graceful enough when she was alone, appeared to wallow in the sea like a clumsy tub, and the frigates began to gain on her. If she couldn't inch close enough to the land to be protected by the batteries of shore-based artillery, she would be sunk within sight of her goal.

Billy caught his breath when a sudden flash illuminated one side of the leading frigate. Then there was a roar, and he released his breath when two cannonballs fell short of the *Marilyn*.

The shore batteries responded to the challenge, opening fire on the intruders. Heavy iron balls whistled through the air over the brig's sails, and the battle was joined. The *Marilyn*, the prize for which the two sides contended, continued to make her way toward port, moving with the maddening pace of a snail.

The shots of the shore batteries fell far short of the frigates. But, Billy saw, they forced the commanders of the two British ships to behave more cautiously. First one, then the other, tacked sharply to starboard, in an obvious maneuver. They hoped to draw close enough to the *Marilyn* to force the land-based batteries to suspend their fire for fear of hitting the merchantman.

The master of the brig was equal to the situation. He subtly tacked a little to port, just enough to avoid being caught in a direct cross fire. And the move cost him no more than a tiny decrease in his already slow speed.

Again volleys were exchanged, as the frigates fired on the *Marilyn* and the shore batteries tried to drive off the enemy. The next hour was a nightmare for Billy. He could see huge crowds on shore now, and although he couldn't hear the cheers and shouts, he realized that people were waving frantic encouragement. It was good to know that, even though the brig was in mortal peril, Americans by the thousands were hoping and praying she would reach her goal.

The frigates were tacking frequently now, following a zigzag course in an attempt to elude the fire of the artillery. But their own shots were landing closer and closer to the *Marilyn,* and it seemed as though they were sure to find their target at any moment.

Then, miraculously, the brig entered the haven of Boston Harbor. The artillery thundered a welcome, bonfires were lighted on shore, and the disappointed enemy frigates were forced to turn away.

Billy felt weak and enjoyed only a moment of elation. One small victory had been won, but for each American merchantman that reached port, at least six others were lost. America was paying a terrible price in men and ships for the vital manufactured goods she needed. But she had no choice. She was fighting for her very life.

Twelve British warships dominated the Great Lakes as completely as the Royal Navy controlled the Atlantic Ocean. They sailed where they pleased, riding the waters of Lake Huron above Fort Detroit and making it a virtual certainty that, at war's end, the Michigan Territory would belong to Great Britain. They went where they pleased on Lake Erie, threatening Ohio. It was only a matter of time, the pessimists agreed, before they sailed into Lake Ontario and carried troops to march south through New York.

One man thought the enemy could be beaten on the Great Lakes and was so persuasive that President Madison wearily agreed to let him do what he could. Oliver Hazard Perry was only twenty-eight years old, the youngest captain in the United States Navy, but he had already acquired impressive credentials. He had served under his father, also a captain, against the Barbary pirates. And he had an unbounded, ferocious faith in the future of his country.

No one in Washington City believed that Perry and less than one thousand men could accomplish the mission assigned to them. "Perry," said the experts, "is mad. He has no ships. How does he expect to beat the British—with his bare hands?"

Undismayed by official and unofficial gloom, Perry and his men went to work in the autumn of 1812. First, the sailors became lumbermen and cut down tall straight oaks that grew in the forests on the southern shore of Lake Erie. They slept in the open, on the ground, and when the weather became cold, they made simple log huts for themselves.

"Keep busy, boys," the Captain told them, "and you won't notice the weather."

When there was enough planking on hand, the sailors became carpenters. Perry acted as his own naval architect, and gradually through the winter of 1812-13 and the chilly spring that followed a fleet of sturdy warships began to take shape. The Captain sent a letter to Washington City saying he was building six schooners, a sloop, and a brig. Responsible, older men merely shook their heads and wished the President would stop wasting manpower and money.

The task Perry faced was enormous. Kegs of nails and tools, canvas for sails, food and equipment and supplies had to be carted to Lake Erie from the cities of the seaboard. Wagons carried the stores, but heavy snows blocked the roads in December.

"Operations will have to be suspended," they said in Washington City.

But they didn't know Oliver Perry. "Bring in what we need by sled," he told men whom he sent to the cities. "And hurry, boys! Every day is precious!"

By the spring of 1813, when the snow vanished, the eight ships were in the water. Then cannon and iron balls and gunpowder were needed. "My fleet won't be ready for another few months," the Captain wrote to his superiors. "But, in the meantime, we need gunnery practice."

Work began soon after dawn each morning on the little fleet. Masts were cut, trimmed, and put in place. The interiors of the ships were finished. And promptly at four o'clock every afternoon all other activities were suspended, and the men shot at targets set up for them in small boats on the lake. Eventually they became proficient gunners, but Perry wasn't satisfied. "You can do better," he said. "We'll work for an extra hour tonight."

Officials in Washington City could scarcely believe that a fleet had materialized in Ohio. Experts made the journey west to investigate, and their worst fears were confirmed. Perry's ships were graceful, to be sure, and seemed seaworthy. But they were miniature versions of the mighty vessels that plied the Atlantic.

"Very handsome, Captain," a member of the Navy Board of Commissioners said. "But how do you expect midget ships to fight a real sea war?"

"The Great Lakes aren't the ocean, sir," Perry replied. "Ships carrying crews of one thousand men would be too cumbersome here. I've deliberately built a fleet of smaller, more maneuverable ships. Each of them will carry between one hundred and three hundred men."

"I hope," the Commissioner said dubiously, "that you know what you're doing."

Oliver Perry looked much younger than his twenty-eight years when he grinned. "I hope so, too," he said, and then laughed confidently. No matter what anyone believed, he and his men would soon be ready to prove their worth.

Twenty-five hundred Tennessee militiamen cheered politely when Major General Andrew Jackson rode into camp, although there was little to cheer about. It had rained day and night for a week, and the men had nothing to protect them from the elements but their own sodden blankets. Food supplies were short, and there was no sign of the provisions that had been promised the troops. Two thousand reinforcements, long overdue, had not yet made their appearance, either.

As for the new commander, he looked far more like an invalid than a general capable of leading his regiments into battle against British-supplied Indian warriors who outnumbered his own forces by at least ten to one. Andrew Jackson's face was deathly pale, he still carried his heavily bandaged left arm in a sling, and an aide had to help him dismount.

He shook his head for a moment, to clear it, and then spoke in a harsh, high-pitched voice that grated on the ears of his listeners. "Boys," he said, "I reckon you'd rather be home with your families. So would I. But we're here to make certain the Fort Mims massacre isn't repeated, and here we'll stay until the savages sue for a lasting peace.

"I wish I could promise you beef and bread, but the supply wagons have been delayed somewhere. So we'll have to tighten our belts. I wish I could give you clean tents, but you'll have to cut brush for your own lean-to shelters. One of these days we'll have a little sunshine, and then you can dry out your blankets.

"I can promise you only one thing—action, and plenty of it! I aim to stay in the wilderness until the Creek and every other tribe agrees to let American settlers live peacefully, without fear."

When the militiamen started to applaud, Jackson raised his hand for silence. "Save your energy," he said curtly. "You'll need it."

To the astonishment of the men, he sat down on a rock and began to eat a meal of plain soldiers' fare, sour pickled beef and hard biscuits. Later he toured the bivouac with his close friend and cavalry commander, Colonel John Coffee. And that night, in spite of his infirmity, he slept in the open, with only one blanket to shield him.

Coffee, the infantry leaders, and the members of the General's staff shared the hardships of the troops, too. And the next morning, as the men broke camp and began their long march toward the land of their foes, a new spirit swept through the ranks. "This general," the men told each other, "doesn't think he's better than we are. He's one of us!"

The rain was still falling, and the militiamen were cold, wet, and hungry. But Andrew Jackson rode at the head of the column. They had confidence in him, and soon their voices were raised in defiant song.

CHAPTER NINE

The *Constitution* was far from home as she cruised the waters of the South Atlantic, off the coast of Brazil. But not one of the hundreds of veteran seamen who made up her crew complained. A few had been uneasy when Commodore Hull had been promoted to the Board of Navy Commissioners in Washington City, but her new commander, Commodore William Bainbridge, was as tough and experienced as his predecessor.

In some ways, the sailors told each other, he was even more of a hunter. He had started out from the United States in command of a squadron of ships and, while visiting various West Indian islands, had sent off his smaller vessels, one by one, when he had learned there were British sloops in the area. He himself was after far bigger game—a glittering trophy that had sent him southward across the Equator.

Somewhere in these waters was one of the most powerful frigates in the Royal Navy. *H.M.S. Java* was bound for India, carrying the new governor of Bombay. Bainbridge intended to find and destroy her, even though she was a huge ship of more than one thousand tons. The crew of the *Constitution* remained on the alert day and night, with a lookout constantly stationed in the crow's nest, high above the rigging. Gun crews slept beside their cannon, and some of the sailors claimed that the Commodore never slept.

That was an exaggeration, of course. But it was true

119

that William Bainbridge spent approximately twenty hours out of every twenty-four on his quarterdeck, even eating his meals at his post. "The British must be made to understand they no longer rule the seas," he told his crew in an order-of-the-day. "There's only one way to convince them. We must seek and sink the proudest ships in her Navy, wherever they dare to sail."

His hunt appeared fruitless, a waste of time and effort. The expanses of the Atlantic were vast, and he was searching for a British needle in an endless salt-water haystack. But at last his grim patience paid dividends when the master of a Dutch merchantman whose path crossed that of the *Constitution* told him that a large British warship had been sighted less than twenty-four hours earlier.

Bainbridge quickly but carefully plotted the *Java's* probable course, then estimated the spot at which he might be able to overtake her. Then, confident of his ship, his men, and himself, he started off under full sail for a rendezvous with destiny. "If my figures are right, and if the wind holds," he told his officers, "we'll find our quarry in about thirty-six hours."

The wind held, and thirty-four and one-half hours later, on December 20, 1812, a shout from the lookout electrified the crew. Thirty-eight-year-old William Bainbridge kicked off his boots, climbed up the crow's nest himself, and smiled as he descended to the quarterdeck.

"Strip for action," he told his first lieutenant. "All hands to battle stations!"

Bugles sounded, and seamen leaped to their posts. All gear that could be moved was taken below, and buckets of sand were carried up to the decks for purposes of putting out fires that might start when fire was exchanged with the enemy. Gunports were lowered, and the muzzles of the *Constitution's* forty-four great cannon peered out across the open water.

Thousands of miles from home, an American man-of-war was deliberately challenging a mighty representative of the strongest Navy in the world. A sultry breeze kept the *Constitution's* sails filled, and Bainbridge tacked frequently in order to reach a point south of his foe. He guessed that the *Java's* captain would prefer to avoid an engagement in order to protect the important diplomat he carried on board. But the American planned to force a fight and cannily placed himself between his enemy and the Brazilian coast, off to the west. There was no escape for the *Java* either to the south or west.

The members of the *Constitution's* gun crews hauled cannonballs into place, arranging them in neat mounds, then went below for bags of gunpowder, which they placed on the deck behind iron shields to prevent explosion and fire in case of an enemy hit. Then, to their surprise, the ship's cooks appeared with smoking joints of meat, bread, and mugs of thick, hot soup. Commodore Bainbridge, like Commodore Hull before him, believed that American seamen fought best on full stomachs.

Tension mounted slowly as the two ships drew closer together, and at last Bainbridge estimated that they were within cannon range of each other. "Hoist our distinguishing pennant," he ordered.

The Stars and Stripes of the United States was run up to the topgallants, and the sailors cheered.

There was a long, dramatic wait. If the *Java* failed to reply, it would be an indication that her captain hoped to run away. But he could not honorably refuse the demand for a duel, and when Bainbridge, watching the British quarterdeck through his glasses, saw the Union Jack being hoisted, he waited no longer.

"Gun crews stand ready!" he called.

"Aye, aye, sir!"

"Port gun number one, fire for range!" the Commodore

ordered just as the Union Jack reached the British warship's topgallants.

A single cannon sounded, and a moment later a heavy ball crashed into the sea no more than fifty feet beyond the prow of the *Java*. Even on a test shot, the American gunners were displaying remarkable accuracy.

"Shorten your range," Bainbridge called to his gunnery lieutenant, "and fire at will!"

"Very good, sir." The officer repeated the instructions to his section chiefs as he and two younger lieutenants moved up and down the line of port cannon, directing the lowering of the barrels' elevation by a fraction of an inch.

Bainbridge, balancing on his quarterdeck with his feet planted apart, continued to watch the enemy through his glass. The two great ships were sailing parallel to each other now, at approximately the same cruising speed, and each was able to rake the other with broadsides. Bainbridge, seeing the gunports lowered on the *Java's* second deck, felt a cold chill move up and down his spine and knew a moment of kinship with the British captain.

Both were far from friendly ports, far from any safe haven into which a battered warship could limp for repairs. This would be a battle to the death.

At that instant the port guns of the *Constitution* erupted in volcanic fury, and the *Java* was raked from prow to stern. Iron balls crashed onto her main deck, and at least three made gaping holes in her hull. The American frigate had drawn first blood.

While the gun crews hastily swabbed out their cannon with wads of thick cloth tied to the ends of stout wooden poles, it was the British vessel's turn. Bainbridge held his breath as he saw twenty almost simultaneous flashes and heard the roar of the enemy's cannon.

Then he exhaled slowly and exchanged an incredulous glance with his first lieutenant, who stood beside him.

Some of the British guns had fired short, some long, some wide of the mark. Not one of the *Java's* guns had come anywhere near its target. British mastery of the seven seas was based on a myth, it appeared.

Again the *Constitution's* port batteries fired, and again they wreaked havoc. Two balls ripped through the *Java's* rigging, leaving sails hanging limply, and others had dug deep furrows in her smooth decks. A fire was blazing aft, on her main deck, and sailors were hastily trying to bring the blaze under control.

Bainbridge felt a twinge of pity for the enemy, but there was more grim work to be done. "Tack to port," he directed as the *Java* necessarily slowed her sailing speed. "Then we'll turn and give the starboard gunners a chance."

The port batteries fired one more devastating round before the *Constitution*, exercising her maneuver brilliantly, crossed the bow of the British ship. The *Java* tried to take evasive action but was moving too sluggishly now to escape, and the *Constitution* swung about again.

The American starboard gun crews were as expert as their comrades, and two sharp volleys left the *Java* badly crippled. She kept up a steady fire, too, but only one cannonball struck the Yankee hull obliquely and fell harmlessly into the sea. "Old Ironsides" was living up to her name.

The battle continued for another forty-five minutes, but the outcome was no longer in doubt. Several fires were raging on the *Java*, and when the *Constitution's* port gunners once again took up their task, they concentrated their fire on the enemy's masts. Two shots struck the base of the mainmast simultaneously, while a third literally sheared it twenty feet high in an astonishing display of accurate gunnery.

Listing badly to starboard, her mainmast gone and two fires raging out of control, the *Java* had become a floating hulk. Bainbridge studied the action on her quarterdeck, then called sharply, "Cease fire!"

The order was repeated to the gun crews, and the cannon fell silent just as the Union Jack was struck and a white flag of surrender raised. Two of the British warship's long-boats had been reduced to kindling, but the remaining two were lowered into the sea, and men began to pile into them.

The waters were a clear, tropical blue-green, and from his quarterdeck Commodore Bainbridge could see the churning, the swiftly darting shapes that meant there were sharks in the vicinity. "Lower all boats—including my own gig—to take off survivors!" he ordered sharply.

Men whose duty it had been to destroy now worked furiously to save human lives. Bainbridge saw an elegantly dressed gentleman being helped into a boat and guessed correctly that the governor-elect of Bombay would soon be his prisoner. His mouth felt dry when he watched the wounded being lowered into longboats. "Tell the surgeons to stand by," he directed.

Miraculously, the *Constitution* had emerged from the battle virtually unscathed. Only one enemy cannonball had done slight damage aft, on the main deck, where a few planks would have to be replaced. The task would occupy the ship's carpenters for no more than a half-hour.

The last to leave the *Java* was her captain, wearing his full-dress uniform and the sword he would hand to his conqueror. As he was being rowed across the open sea, his ship began to settle, very slowly and gradually.

Commodore Bainbridge stood motionless on his quarter-deck, watching the *Java* sink. No true seafarer could feel elation when a ship died, even an enemy he had himself destroyed. But a far deeper sense of satisfaction filled Bainbridge. He had beaten a powerful British warship in a fair battle, and realized that now, more than ever, "Old

Ironsides" would hold a special place in the affections of the American people.

News of the *Constitution*'s great victory helped to dispel the gloom that was universal throughout the United States in 1813. Other triumphs at sea did a great deal, too, to improve the country's spirits. Two of Bainbridge's former lieutenants, called "the Sea Tiger's cubs" by the press, won impressive victories of their own. Captain Stephen Decatur, commanding the frigate *United States,* outfought and captured a larger British warship, the *Macedonian.* Young Captain James Lawrence, in the small frigate *Hornet,* defeated and captured a British vessel of approximately the same size and strength, the *Peacock.*

Other Yankee frigates were making good news, too, among them the *Constellation* and the *Wasp.* But, in spite of the victories won by a handful of American ships, in spite of superb American seamanship and magnificently accurate American gunnery, the huge Royal Navy doggedly maintained its tight blockade.

In June, 1813, while the Creek were planning their raid on Fort Mims and Captain Perry was putting the finishing touches on the ships of his Great Lakes flotilla, Captain James Lawrence was given the difficult task of trying to break the British blockade of Boston. He put to sea in the *Chesapeake,* whose encounter with the *Leopard* had been one of the major incidents leading to the outbreak of the war.

The *Chesapeake* fared no better now. She encountered the *Shannon,* a slightly larger British frigate, just outside Boston Harbor, and in the vicious duel that followed the Yankee warship was cut to pieces. Lawrence himself was mortally wounded, and as he lay dying on his quarterdeck, he begged his officers and men, "Don't give up the ship."

His dying words became a rallying cry for the entire nation. The cause of the United States appeared to be growing more hopeless with each passing day, but the sense of panic lessened as men told each other, *"Don't give up the ship!"*

By the end of June, Perry's little fleet was ready for action, and he sailed off into Lake Erie to search for the enemy, his flagship, the *Niagara,* in the van. He didn't have far to hunt: a few days later he encountered the British Great Lakes fleet at the entrance to Put-in-Bay, at the western end of Lake Erie, just off the town of Sandusky, Ohio.

The long months of preparation were at an end. "Make ready to attack," Perry ordered, and as the signal flags were raised to the topgallants of his twin-masted ship, the members of his staff marveled at his calm.

The advantages of using small, easily maneuverable ships quickly became apparent as Perry formed his flotilla in a single line and headed toward the enemy. He accomplished the move in a remarkably short time, before the larger, more cumbersome British vessels were able to arrange themselves in battle position.

But the Royal Navy units made up in fire power what they lacked in mobility. Their huge cannon roared continuously, and only their inferior marksmanship saved the Americans from quick destruction.

"Close in," Perry ordered, and sailed his flotilla closer to the enemy so his own guns would be more effective. He knew precisely what he was doing and coolly had made up his mind to run a deliberate risk. Although his ships might well suffer a more severe beating at close quarters, the odds that he could destroy his foes were much improved.

In order to compensate for the greater size and strength of the Royal Navy flotilla, Perry kept his own fleet in constant motion. He tacked constantly, sometimes opening and sometimes closing the gap between his ships, which wove in and out of the British line like a needle and thread plunging repeatedly through a piece of cloth.

The American gunners kept up an incessant stream of fire, selecting and concentrating on their targets with great care. At times the smoke was so thick as the two forces pounded at each other that it was impossible to see across the water, and the cannoneers enjoyed brief respites. Their guns grew cooler, and then they hurled themselves into the fray again.

Perry's tactics became still bolder, and he isolated the largest of the British ships, neatly cutting it out of the enemy line, then surrounding it with his own light ships and subjecting it to a frightful battering. He repeated the maneuver with the second ship in the British line, then the third, and each time he was successful.

But he was forced to pay a high price for his audacity. His own ship became the prime British target, and not even his swift and delicate maneuvering could save her from a drubbing. Heavy balls crashed onto her decks and opened holes in her hull. One of his masts toppled, and his sails were slashed to ribbons. But he remained indifferent to his own safety and continued to direct the entire American operation from his quarterdeck with the imperviousness to danger of a genius—or a madman.

The battle wore on, and as the hours passed, Perry's ship limped more and more painfully. Finally it became impossible for her to escape the wrath of the British, and several direct hits just above the waterline sent a long shudder through her from prow to stern.

Captain Perry promptly sent the other American vessels behind his own ship, using her as a shield to protect them while they regrouped. "All officers and men will evacuate at once in the longboats," he ordered, and the men reluctantly but promptly obeyed.

The ship began to settle lower and still lower in the water. Then a fire broke out aft, and when it blew up a powder magazine, the fate of the American vessel was sealed.

Perry still stood on his quarterdeck, watching the men rowing to the safety of the other ships and ignoring the enemy shots that continued to rip into his hull.

"Sir," his squadron signal lieutenant asked as the last longboat was lowered, "are you coming with us?"

Captain Perry shook his head. "Not quite yet. I want the enemy to keep concentrating on me until everyone else is safe." He had to raise his voice to make himself heard, but his tone was quietly conversational. "Have my gig put into the water, and I'll join you when I can."

The officer didn't want to leave him but had no choice. A direct order from a superior had to be obeyed.

Perry, alone on the quarterdeck of the sinking ship, analyzed his situation. Two of the British ships had been sunk, a third was a semi-derelict, and the fire-power of a fourth was much reduced. So far, he knew, he was ahead. His casualties had been light, and the longboats had reached the other American ships. No one had become panicky, and ultimate victory was within grasp.

The time had come for him to leave. Taking a last look around him, he went to the main deck, which was already awash. Then he stepped into his little gig, which was scarcely larger than a small rowboat, cut her loose with a knife he took from a boot-top, and casually started to row in the direction of the nearest American schooner.

British small arms fire fell around him, but he ignored it as he rowed with long, powerful strokes. A bullet passed through his hat and several others splintered the wood of the boat's hull. But Oliver Perry appeared to be leading a charmed life. He reached the schooner, strong hands hauled him aboard, and he brushed off his uniform as he

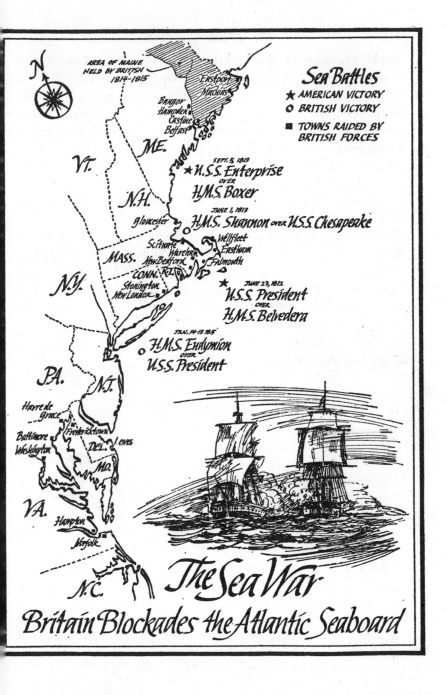

The Sea War

Britain Blockades the Atlantic Seaboard

made his way to the quarterdeck. There, without interruption, he took command of his squadron again.

His men, heartened by his miraculous escape, fought with redoubled vigor. British fire was becoming feebler, and Perry ordered the gun crews on all of his ships to spare neither ammunition nor powder. The barrels of some American cannon became so hot that the weapons literally melted and became useless.

Finally, after a battle that had lasted the better part of the day, the battered enemy flagship lowered the Union Jack and hoisted a white flag. At that instant control of the Great Lakes passed from British hands into American.

The laconic message that Perry—soon to be promoted to commodore for his triumph—sent to Washington City became famous overnight. "We have met the enemy," he wrote, "and they are ours: two ships, two brigs, one schooner and one sloop."

At last America had cause to rejoice.

CHAPTER TEN

Major General Andrew Jackson was having his troubles, and his close friends were afraid his temper would soon explode. It was true that he had won several relatively minor engagements against the Creek, but the victories gave him little satisfaction. The savages were growing stronger, and he had yet to meet them in a decisive battle.

His problems, however, were no farther away than his own camp, deep in the Southern wilderness of forests and swamps. His corps had grown to approximately forty-five-hundred men, most of them infantry. But the quartermasters in Washington City and Tennessee appeared to have forgotten their existence.

Only one wagon train had arrived with food supplies since he had started his campaign. For weeks the men had been living off the land, but game was scarce, fish had disappeared from the rivers, and corn, wheat, and other grains were non-existent. Ammunition was running low, and so was gunpowder. In order to get bullets for his small artillery weapons, four little howitzers, he had to send a squadron of Colonel John Coffee's cavalry on a journey of more than one hundred miles to the north.

The men had no spare blankets, and their only clothes were the buckskins they wore on their backs. As yet no one had been forced to go barefooted, but boots and moccasins were wearing perilously thin.

The militiamen were hungry, and many, who had enlisted for a period of only ninety days, began to grumble that they intended to go home as soon as their period of present service expired. Andy Jackson paid no official attention to the complaints, but every evening after the day's march he went through the bivouac, stopping frequently to chat informally with the men. Some were cheered by his presence and found it easy to laugh and joke with him. Others, particularly the members of several units from the mountains of eastern Tennessee, remained surly and silent in his presence.

One company of mountaineer militiamen stared at the General with dull eyes when he strolled into their bivouac soon after making camp on an evening when the whole corps was near exhaustion. The corps had marched more than twenty-five miles that day in pursuit of the elusive Creek, and even the huge John Coffee, who accompanied the General on his rounds, looked ready to drop.

Jackson, his left arm still in a sling, managed to smile. "Well, boys," he asked, "have you had enough exercise for today?"

There was a long silence, then a thin youth of about twenty stepped forward. "We don't mind walking, General, and we're always spoiling for a fight. But our belts won't hold up our breeches much longer if we don't get some food!"

Andrew Jackson nodded sympathetically. "Right now," he confided, "I wouldn't mind eating roasted quartermaster. But one of these days the supply wagons will catch up with us."

"When?" the young recruit demanded boldly, egged on by his comrades.

"Blamed if I can tell you," the General answered candidly. "All I know is that when the supplies reach us, you'll get your fair share of food, every last one of you."

The men glanced at each other, and again the recruit was urged to speak for the others. "It's not fair."

"That's one of the troubles with war," Jackson countered. "They're never fair. Soldiers are expected to put up with the bad as well as the good."

The youth stared at him sullenly, in open rebellion. "I'm hungry!"

Andy Jackson was aware of the whole group's tension as he returned the young man's gaze. "At the moment, son," he said, "the best I can do is share my own supper with you."

To the astonishment of Colonel Coffee and the men, he squatted, took a handful of peanuts from his pocket, and placed them in two piles.

"Here, son," he said, thrusting some of the nuts into the youth's hand and putting the rest back into his pocket.

No one spoke, no one moved as the General slowly made his way back to the lean-to shelter that his aides had built for him.

The story quickly made the rounds of the camp, as Jackson knew it would. For the next two weeks the men remained quiet, suffering hardships without complaint. During this time they fought several skirmishes with the Creek; neither side gained a decisive advantage, and the spirit of discontent flared again.

At last a long supply train arrived, but the men groaned aloud when they learned that most of the carts contained ammunition and powder. Only a few of the wagons were laden with food.

"Our bellies may be empty," General Jackson declared, "but at least our rifles will be filled. And that's what matters. We're down here to fight, not stuff ourselves at banquets."

Less than forty-eight hours later he learned that some of the men disagreed violently.

The column halted its march at noon beside the banks of a clear, swift-running brook, and the General, like so many of his troops, retired to the shade of a grove of trees and threw himself to the ground.

His brief rest was interrupted by the usually good-natured John Coffee, whose face was dark. "General," he said abruptly, "the rear guard has deserted!"

Jackson struggled to his feet.

"A full battalion of militia has started for home. Two or three who refused to go with the others said their excuse was that their enlistments will expire in two weeks—and it'll take them just about that long to reach their demobilization centers in Tennessee."

For a moment Jackson stood very still. As he quickly realized, his entire expedition had been placed in jeopardy. Unless he met the challenge—and won—other troops by the thousands would soon follow the deserters.

"I'll borrow your rifle," he said to a nearby soldier. Inspecting the weapon to make certain it was loaded, he walked to his horse and, unaided, vaulted into the saddle.

He had ridden a half-mile by the time Colonel Coffee and two squadrons of cavalry caught up with him.

"What in blazes do you think you're doing, Andy?" Coffee, a lifetime friend and a relative by marriage, was so upset he forgot to address the General by his title.

Jackson turned in the saddle, his smile frosty. "Right now," he said, "I'm going to save my breath because I aim to ride across open country instead of using the road."

Suiting action to words, he headed across the fields at a gallop. He did not slow his pace until he had completed his shortcut and once again reached the only road in the area.

"I reckon I've headed them off," he said as he dismounted.

Coffee and the cavalrymen watched him in shocked silence as he laid the barrel of his rifle across his saddle, gripping it with his uninjured hand.

"Clear the road," he said. "I hear them coming, and I don't want any of you hurt."

The cavalry squadrons continued to fill the road behind him.

"John, I just gave an order," Jackson said irritably. "I want it obeyed."

Colonel Coffee reluctantly gave the necessary commands, and the squadrons moved off into the fields, one to the left of the road, the other to the right.

A gray-haired, crippled Nashville lawyer stood alone, his rifle pointed in the direction of the two hundred and fifty heavily armed militiamen who kicked up clouds of dust as they marched toward him.

The leaders saw him, recognized their General, and the ragged column straggled to a halt.

"Boys," Jackson called in a loud, clear voice, speaking distinctly so all of the would-be deserters could hear him, "I reckon I'm more surprised at seeing you here than you are seeing me. I hear tell that you aren't happy with the way this war is going, and you want to quit. It's my duty to remind you that you're serving on active duty until the first day of the month.

"If you want to leave on the day that your enlistments expire, if you want to desert your country and your neighbors in a time of terrible crisis, I reckon I can't stop you. Cowards always run away.

"But you're not leaving until your enlistments *do* expire. I could have followed you with the whole corps. I could hang your leaders for mutiny. I could even have all of you thrown into a prison stockade.

"I won't do any of those things. I haven't come down to the Alabama Territory to quarrel with boys from Tennessee. I'm here to whip the Creek, and so are you. So you can just turn around and skedaddle back down the road."

The men shuffled their feet, glanced at each other, and

then stared down at the dust. The sun overhead was almost unbearably hot, and there was no sound but the unexpected chirping of a bird perched on a branch of a stunted yellow pine.

One of the soldiers in the front rank gained the courage to call, "Suppose we don't, General? Suppose we insist on going home right now?"

There was a harsh, metallic ring in Andrew Jackson's voice as he replied, "You'll have to advance over my dead body, boys. There's only one bullet in this rifle. And you can plainly see I'm not able to reload it. But that bullet will land between the eyes of a deserter. And I'll take care of a few more with my sword before you kill me. Advance at your own risk!"

No one moved.

"I don't have all day to chat with you, boys. Back to the corps with you, and don't waste any more of your time or mine."

The almost incredible courage of one man had saved the situation. The battalion turned and started back in the direction from which it had come.

Jackson mounted his horse, the cavalry joined him, and he fell back to the rear of the column with John Coffee. To the Colonel's amazement, he was chuckling quietly.

"What's so blamed funny, Andy?"

"Take a good look at this rifle I borrowed, John. It's loaded, right enough, but it's so old the hammer fell off when I was riding across the fields. If those troops had advanced, I couldn't have fired at them!"

President Madison intervened personally to ease General Jackson's plight. A full regiment of Regular Army troops, one thousand strong, was ordered to join Jackson and stiffen the backbone of his corps. Equally important, urgent orders at last turned the creaking wheels of a government unaccustomed to coping with emergency situations, and vast quantities of beef and flour, mutton and corn, venison and barley were dispatched and carried to the hungry soldiers in the South.

Meanwhile the war in the North had taken a somewhat better turn. Madison and his most trusted aide, Secretary Monroe, discussed the situation late one evening in the Executive Mansion as they studied reports from the commanders in the field.

"The British position at Fort Detroit became exposed after Perry's victory on the Great Lakes," the President said, smiling for the first time in many weeks. "So General Harrison has been able to recapture the post."

"Let's hope," the Secretary of State replied, "that this is the turning point."

For a short time the Americans thought they scented real victory in the air. William Henry Harrison pursued a column of British troops and Indians across the Canadian border. In a small but significant battle that followed, his troops killed Tecumseh. The great savage's death destroyed the confederation of Indian nations, as no other chief was capable of welding the tribes together.

Andrew Jackson, still pursuing the Creek, heard the news with grim satisfaction. "Now," he said, "we can deal with one tribe at a time."

Newspapers in the major American cities again predicted that an invasion of Canada was in the offing and that Britain would be forced to sue for peace after Montreal and Quebec fell into Yankee hands. The new spirit of optimism soared when—for unexplained reasons—two divisions of Redcoats were withdrawn from Halifax early in the autumn of 1813 and sent to Europe.

Neither General Harrison nor General James Wilkinson, the overall commander in the Northern sector, was able to capitalize on the recapture of Fort Detroit, however. Wilkinson spent so much time reorganizing and regrouping his forces that winter came before he was ready to march. To the disgust of the energetic "young generals," Winfield Scott and Jacob Brown, he went into winter quarters.

Harrison was unable to advance deeper into Canada without support from Wilkinson and withdrew to Fort Detroit. The bubble of American hopes burst and vanished. But everywhere, from New York to Nashville, from Baltimore and Charleston to Louisville, men told each other, "When spring comes, we'll win a total victory." Even the New Englanders opposed to the war stopped carping.

Then, suddenly, events beyond the control of the United States created a new situation.

One night early in 1814, an American sloop, homeward bound from Europe, managed to slip past the blockading warships of the British fleet and dock at Baltimore. A representative of the State Department slipped ashore quietly, a heavy dispatch box under his arm, and hired the fastest horse he could find. Alone and unheralded, he thundered down the road to Washington City.

The Secretary of State and his wife were entertaining a few guests when the young diplomat arrived, and Monroe went into the library with him. A quarter of an hour later, the white-faced Secretary emerged, carrying the dispatch box, and informed his guests that urgent business required his immediate attention. Offering no further explanation, he went out into the night.

Too anxious to wait for his carriage, he walked the three blocks to the Executive Mansion.

Only a few lamps were burning in the building, and Captain Talbot, Madison's military aide, was apologetic. "I'm sorry, Mr. Secretary," he said, "but the President went to bed an hour ago. He's asleep."

"Then wake him up!" There was a note of urgency in

Monroe's voice. "I'll wait for him in his office. And while you're at it, Captain, double the guard here."

The startled Talbot hurried away, wise enough to ask no questions.

A few minutes later President Madison, hair rumpled and eyes still puffy, walked into the office where his impatient Secretary of State was waiting.

"The worst of all catastrophes has happened," Monroe said, wasting no words. "Napoleon has fallen!"

President Madison, jarred wide awake, tugged at the sash of his dressing gown.

"There was a tremendous battle at Leipzig several weeks ago, and the combined armies of Russia, Austria, and Prussia crushed the strongest army the French could put into the field. Napoleon retreated to Paris, but his enemies followed him, and were joined by a British force."

"Now we know," the President murmured, "why those Redcoat divisions were withdrawn from Halifax."

Secretary Monroe spread the contents of the dispatch box on the desk. "Napoleon's attempts to save himself were fantastic, but it was no use. He's been forced to abdicate and has been sent to the island of Elba in the Mediterranean to spend the rest of his days in exile."

Madison glanced quickly through the documents. "France has surrendered."

"She has, Mr. President."

"That means the British will be able to throw their entire force into the war against us." Madison continued to study the papers. "She can treble the size of her blockading fleet. Is that correct?"

"It's even worse than that, sir. Scores of armed transports are now available to the Royal Navy, too."

"And no doubt they'll be used." Madison looked very old and weary. "Veteran troops by the thousands—troops that have fought and beaten Napoleon's finest divisions—will be sent across the Atlantic."

The two men responsible, above all others, for the safety and security of the United States stared at each other for a moment. Suddenly Monroe laughed harshly. "I see by these papers that Lord Wellesley—probably the finest soldier in the world—has been made the Duke of Wellington. I can't help wondering what will happen if he decides to take command of the British armies in the New World in person."

"Regardless of whether he comes himself, his best troops are certain to pour across the Atlantic in a crimson avalanche," the President replied soberly.

Monroe shuddered. "Who will face them? Frightened militiamen who are still learning the basic art of soldiering, no doubt." He spread his hands, grimacing. "And who'll lead our defenders? We have Wilkinson, who has yet to win a battle against inferior forces. There's Harrison, who is able enough against Indians, but has scarcely been able to hold his own against second-rate British troops. And there's the Nashville lawyer, Jackson, who sends insolent letters to the War Department as he chases savages through the South. This is a nightmare, Mr. President."

James Madison composed himself. "We shall do our best in the days ahead," he said, "and pray that the Lord will favor the cause of men who want only their own freedom."

CHAPTER ELEVEN

The Creek built themselves a strong fort at the Horseshoe Bend of the Tallapoosa River. There William Weatherford, their half-breed leader, gathered two thousand of his most effective and courageous warriors, who went to work with a vengeance in order to make the place impregnable. Andrew Jackson advanced toward it slowly through the early months of 1814, demonstrating that his reputation for recklessness was undeserved. Behind him he left a string of strong, fortified posts, each manned by one hundred to three hundred reliable men. If it became necessary for him to retreat, he had established a safe line to the rear.

Twenty-six-hundred Americans, led by Coffee's horsemen, approached the Creek stronghold at the Horseshoe an hour or two before sundown on March 26, 1814, and General Jackson, surveying the ground with several of his senior commanders, realized that Weatherford had chosen a battle site highly favorable to the defenders. The area which the Creek were defending was a peninsula which occupied approximately one hundred acres of rugged terrain. It was virtually impossible to launch an attack by water, as the Tallapoosa, swollen by early spring rains, was flowing too swiftly.

The obvious spot at which to launch the assault was the inner neck of the peninsula, but at that point the Creek had built their massive log fort, with decks and portholes constructed on three levels.

"Even if we can take the fort," Major Lemuel Montgomery of the Regulars said dubiously, "we'll then have to move inch by inch down the peninsula."

Coffee nodded soberly. "At best it's going to be a rough battle. Maybe we ought to lay siege to the place instead and starve the savages out."

Andrew Jackson, pleased because he had finally reached his goal after many months of privation, disagreed cheerfully but vehemently. "Gentlemen," he said, "you don't seem to realize that the Creek have boxed themselves in. When we take the fort—and mind, I said when, not if—they'll have no place to go." He rubbed his left arm, from which the sling had just been removed. "Yonder, tied up at the river's edge a stone's throw from the fort, are the Creek war canoes. Their only hope of escape if we beat them." He summoned an aide. "At suppertime tonight, make the rounds of the battalion campfires and ask for volunteers who'll swim across the river at dawn and carry off the canoes."

The corps ate a hearty meal of beef stew, fried corn cakes, and apples boiled with honey. Then, while the men retired for the night, their General retired to the tent that the quartermasters had finally procured for him, and there he worked out battle tactics in precise detail. The "lawyer from Nashville," the "civilian who knows nothing about war," was demonstrating a remarkable talent for military leadership and was leaving nothing to chance. At four in the morning, after drawing scores of rough sketches to illustrate step-by-step operations, he called in the regimental and battalion commanders. Each was given an assignment, and the General made sure that everyone understood what was expected of him before adjourning the meeting.

Troops were posted in the woods on the far banks of the Tallapoosa, surrounding the peninsula, and Montgomery's regiment of Regulars was given the honor of leading approximately forty percent of the corps in an assault on the fort.

At dawn Colonel Coffee himself supervised the carrying away of the enemy canoes, and although the Creek poured rifle and musket fire at the volunteers, this phase of the operation was carried out successfully, without loss of life. Colonel Coffee was exceptionally nimble and quick for a big man.

By nine o'clock in the morning General Jackson received word that all units had moved into position. His artillery, now consisting of four batteries, came forward and took their places in the forest behind the assault infantry. Then the cannon, the largest of them six-pounders that were incapable of denting the hull of a stout warship, opened fire on the fort and bombarded it steadily for more than an hour.

Operations were halted when the Indians unexpectedly raised a white flag. But when the smoke cleared away it was plain to the General that his foes merely wanted to talk and had no intention of surrendering. The cannonballs had dug harmlessly into the soft wood of the log fort, and the building was virtually intact.

A Creek messenger came out and explained the flag, asking permission for the women and children to be evacuated. Many of the officers, remembering the Fort Mims massacre, wanted to refuse, but the General ignored their views and immediately granted his permission. "The difference between savages and civilized men," he said, "is that we don't make war on the defenseless."

Soldiers who were experienced boatmen were sent across the river in the canoes and began to evacuate the noncombatants. The task was long and tedious and wasn't completed until afternoon. Then, in the brief lull that followed, Andrew Jackson rode forward to the river bank directly opposite the fort, paying no attention to his aides' demands that he not expose himself needlessly to enemy fire. The militiamen and Regulars cheered him as he moved up past them, and he responded by waving to them without smiling. Halting beside the Regulars' vanguard at the peninsula's neck, he said to Major Montgomery, "Signal the charge!"

The blare of bugles echoed through the wilderness, and the Regulars raced forward. Major Montgomery himself was the first to reach the fort, but two Creek sharpshooters brought him down before he could climb to the top of the palisade surrounding the building. A young, recently commissioned ensign of unusual promise, Sam Houston, was the first to scale the wall. Twenty men followed him, then fifty more climbed over the palisade, and a vicious hand-to-hand battle raged for more than a quarter of an hour.

Suddenly Houston reappeared on the lowest deck of the fort, brandishing his sword and shouting. Meanwhile the outer wall was torn down by the infantrymen, and the rest of the regiment raced toward the main fort. The sound of firing increased, and General Jackson sent one regiment of militia to support the Regulars. Then another went into action, with only one kept in reserve.

Heavy rifle fire from the far side of the river indicated that some of the Creek were making a desperate attempt to swim to safety. The General felt he had no choice and committed his last remaining regiment.

Three hundred and fifty of the original attackers had now disappeared into the huge fort. The General, to the dismay of his staff, insisted on riding forward, sword in hand, and pressed through a hole cut in the side of the building.

He saw at once that the battle in that sector appeared to be won and immediately sent a courier down the peninsula to offer honorable terms of surrender to all retreating Creek warriors who would accept it. The messenger was shot, and the braves, taking stands in ravines and gullies, fought with renewed fury.

The General, methodical and calm, sent forward platoons of volunteers to flush them out. But the savages preferred death to surrender, and not until early evening was the last position taken, the last warrior silenced. At seven o'clock the General ordered the buglers to sound a cease-fire.

Prisoners were rounded up and disarmed, wounded soldiers were carried to the tents of the surgeons, and the troops rested on their arms. Casualties were counted, and the General was pleasantly surprised to find that, thanks to his careful planning, casualties were relatively light. Forty-nine men had been killed and one hundred and fifty-eight wounded. The surgeons believed that the vast majority of the injured would recover.

But the losses suffered by the Creek were staggering. More than eight hundred had died, and virtually every prisoner had been wounded. Not one warrior capable of carrying on the fight was found alive.

To Andrew Jackson's intense disappointment, however, Weatherford was not among the dead or wounded and, apparently, had vanished.

But a great surprise was in store for the General. On the day after the battle, while the corps rested, an officer of the guard came to headquarters with word that a man was at the camp perimeter, insisting on seeing General Jackson. He was admitted, and a light-skinned Indian, clad only in buckskin trousers and moccasions, bowed to the victor. "I am Bill Weatherford," he said, speaking excellent English.

Jackson was too startled to reply.

"I've come to give myself up to you. I can oppose you no longer, and am in your power. Do with me what you will."

Ignoring the protests of his aides, the General invited Weatherford into his tent and gave him a cup of brandy-wine. "You're not in my power, Mr. Weatherford," Andy Jackson said quietly. "If I'd captured you, I'd have put you in chains, but you've come to me of your own accord, so I must treat you with the respect that you're due. What do you want?"

"For myself, nothing," Weatherford said softly. "I would continue the fight, but too many of my warriors are dead and cannot be brought to life again. Kill me, if you still seek vengeance. But give food and shelter to our women and children, who have been scattered through the forests with nothing to eat."

"I'll do what I can for them." Jackson hesitated for a moment. "As for you, Mr. Weatherford, I release you unconditionally, on my own authority."

Weatherford was deeply moved. "My people have spoken the truth about you when they have called you a great warrior. I pledge to you that I will do everything in the little power I still hold to turn the thoughts of our elders and those braves still alive to ways of peace."

The General extended his hand. "That's a bargain." He turned to his aide, who gaped as these fiercest of enemies shook hands. "See that Mr. Weatherford is escorted to safety through our lines. Any man who molests him will be court-martialed and shot."

Vanquished and victor looked at each other, two proud men, both of them leaders who had needed to exchange few words in order to achieve a complete mutual understanding. Then Weatherford turned away slowly, his bearing erect, and walked out.

Colonel Coffee, who had watched the scene from the entrance to the tent, came inside, shaking his head. "Andy, have you lost your wits?" he demanded. "You had him right here. We could have hanged him from the nearest tree, but you let him go!"

"We've destroyed the Creek will to fight," the General explained patiently. "But if I had executed their leader, thousands of braves who have taken no part in the war would have marched against us. By releasing Weatherford, I've brought the Indian war in the South to an end. Now we can start doing whatever is needed to protect this part of the country from those British veterans who scare the faint-hearted half to death."

Andrew Jackson's smashing victory over the Creek and the subsequent cession of twenty-three million acres of territory to the United States by the Indian nation was the only cause for cheer in 1814. British troop transports crossed the Atlantic in a steady, unbroken stream, bringing fresh divisions of Redcoats to the New World. Opposition to the war flared again in New England, and representatives of the five states of the region—most of them members of the old Federalist political party that was rapidly losing its influence—met at Hartford.

A few who attended the convention spoke boldly of secession from the Union, but the talk amounted to nothing. The real leaders of New England, men like Daniel Webster and John Quincy Adams, firmly supported President Madison and offered him their unstinting help in the trials yet to come.

The United States did not have long to wait for those trials. A column of British veterans, twelve thousand strong, launched an invasion from Canada, using the Lake Champlain route that had been so hotly contested in the Revolution. Once again the Navy saved the country from catastrophe.

Captain Thomas McDonough hastily put together a fleet of small boats, onto which he loaded every cannon he could find. He sailed up Lake Champlain, met the enemy at Plattsburg, New York, and there fought a ferocious battle. Once again the gunnery of American seamen was superb, and the British suffered a major defeat. The proud corps of Redcoats had to struggle northward through the wilderness, and energetic Yankee militiamen repeated tactics that had so often proved successful in the Revolution.

Troops accustomed to the more formal warfare of European battlefields struggled through unfamiliar forests. Their progress was hampered by Yankee marksmen who hid behind trees and rocks and who inflicted a heavy toll on their enemies. The British high command reluctantly abandoned its plan to take control of the Hudson valley. And the Americans consoled themselves with the knowledge that at least one invasion attempt had been repulsed.

But there were others, as regiment after regiment of British troops continued to cross the ocean under Royal Navy escort. At the height of an Independence Day celebration at Niagara Falls, General Winfield Scott learned that a large Redcoat force was massing for another attempted invasion. Early on the morning of July 5th, his troops and those of General Jacob Brown took the initiative, crossing the Canadian border and launching their own assault before the British had a chance to attack.

The Americans were the victors in a bloody engagement, but the issue had not been settled to the satisfaction of either side. Both of the opposing armies brought up artillery, and a few days later there was a second clash in what became known as the Battle of Lundy's Lane. The crash of cannon was matched by the roar of Niagara Falls, and both sides displayed stubborn courage. The Americans demonstrated that they could fight when ably led, but they weren't strong enough to drive their opponents from the field.

General Scott had suffered heavy losses, and although he had inflicted severe punishment on the Redcoats, too, he knew his danger would be doubled if the enemy brought up reinforcements. Given no real alternative, he withdrew to the American side of Niagara Falls. At the very least, it was good to know that American troops were able to hold their own and that another attempted invasion had been delayed and blunted, perhaps permanently stopped.

But even the most optimistic of the War Hawks in Congress were beginning to recognize the bitter truth that strictly defensive measures would not win the war. Some of the Westerners made speeches suggesting that General Jackson be given command of a fast-moving corps that could capture the major cities of Canada, but professional soldiers laughed at the idea.

Jackson, they said, was still an amateur, and could not be considered in the same class with the rapidly developing Scott. But even Scott, they declared, could not invade Canada, where as many as forty to fifty thousand Redcoats were now stationed.

The War Department sent President Madison a long report soon after the Battle of Lundy's Lane saying that there was now a stalemate in the war. Neither side had been able to gain a decisive advantage, and it was possible, even probable, that the war might drag on for years.

Commodore Hull, now a member of the Navy Board of Commissioners, expressed his opinion of the report in no uncertain terms when he was summoned to the Executive Mansion. "Mr. President," he said emphatically, "the civilians who wrote this nonsense know nothing of war. Our Navy is performing feats of valor that will live in history for hundreds of years. But the blockade of our Atlantic ports is as tight and effective as it was two years ago.

"The Army is taking shape at last. Scott is a good soldier, and Harrison seems fairly efficient. This fellow from Tennessee, Jackson, is rather unorthodox, but I like him. Yet, no matter how effective all three of them may be, they can't prevent the British from landing an invasion force almost any place they please. We have a long coastline, our cities are virtually unprotected, and I swear to you, sir, that the worst is still to come!"

Commodore Hull proved to be a dismayingly accurate prophet. The masters of merchantmen who returned from trading missions to the West Indian Islands and successfully ran the blockade came home with stories that a powerful corps of British Regulars was being assembled in Jamaica under the command of General Sir Edward Pakenham, who had been one of Wellington's most brilliant subordinates in England's long war against the French.

These disturbing reports were confirmed by the few foreign visitors who reached the United States from the Caribbean. One of them, Helmut Klagerholme, a Danish merchant who subsequently became an American citizen, went straight to Secretary Monroe with his information.

"I saw thousands of the troops with my own eyes in the town of Kingston," he said. "And I dined in a tavern there only two tables from Sir Edward himself. He and his men fought Napoleon for many years, and they're the toughest, most self-confident soldiers on earth. They actually use live ammunition and bayonets in their practice field exercises. They make no secret of their belief that they'll take the United States by storm."

President Madison sent an additional division of Regulars to General Jackson, who was instructed to take all measures he deemed necessary for the protection of New Orleans, the smaller towns, and the semi-isolated American forts on the country's southern shores facing the Gulf of Mexico. All America looked southward toward the West Indies and waited anxiously.

While the United States was preoccupied, the British made secret preparations in Canada for the launching of a staggering, unexpected assault. Ships-of-the-line, frigates, sloops, and scores of auxiliary vessels from Halifax and Quebec met at a rendezvous in the Atlantic. There they awaited a smaller squadron from England, which was convoying a powerful Army corps commanded by another veteran of the Napoleonic Wars, General Robert Ross.

The combined units sailed southward, their first destination Washington City. In order to create a diversion, another much smaller force sailed direct from Quebec to the

Maine District and there raided several small towns and fishing villages. Express couriers carried the news to Washington City, where ignorance of the real British intentions was still bliss.

Less than twenty-four hours before Ross's corps was carried up Chesapeake Bay, the masters of several small fishing vessels caught sight of the Royal Navy fleet. They were able to escape their pursuers and carry word to President Madison that a vast British armada was off the coast.

The unprepared War Department frantically assigned the only militia units available to the task of defending Washington City. The head of the Maryland militia, General W. H. Winder, was an unfortunate choice as the commander of the defending forces, and no one knew it better than the President.

"Winder is no soldier!" he declared.

Officials of the War Department were apologetic. "There's no one else at hand to take charge, sir," they explained.

Winder proved inadequate for the task, and the Maryland militia fled in panic after the British corps landed from Chesapeake Bay on the banks of the little Patuxent River. General Ross encountered virtually no opposition as he marched to Washington City. And the United States was forced to endure the supreme humiliation of seeing the Executive Mansion and the Capitol, the government seats of the President and of Congress, put to the torch.

British interest in Washington City was actually slight, however. The small town of a few thousand inhabitants was important only as a symbol, and the burning of its most significant buildings was intended solely as a blow at American pride and spirit. The Redcoats remained for only a few hours and then withdrew.

President Madison showed his tremendous personal courage by returning to the capital immediately, and most government officials and members of Congress went with him.

Painters went to work at the Executive Mansion at once, covering the fire and smoke-streaked timbers with several coats of glistening white paint in order to conceal the nation's shame as quickly as possible. Dolley Madison, as usual, provided just the right note of gentle humor by referring to the place as The White House.

The President knew now, from first-hand experience, that there were incompetents in high places, and one of his first acts when he reached Washington City was to order a thorough reorganization of the government. He had found there was one man, above all others, who could be trusted to discharge any and every responsibility. So he asked James Monroe to assume the burden of Secretary of War in addition to his duties as Secretary of State.

The weight of the double load would have crushed an ordinary man, but Monroe quietly accepted its challenge. Then, throwing himself into his work with a fury that left subordinates gasping, he started sending cannon and ammunition, men and supplies to the great city of Baltimore, the real object of the British attack.

CHAPTER TWELVE

Baltimore, in 1814, was the fourth largest city in the United States. President Madison had called her "the heart and soul of the American midlands," and his description was accurate. Located on the delta of the Patapsco River, she had many deep-water channels that fed into Chesapeake Bay, and her wharves and warehouses ran for hundreds of yards along her waterfront. She was the principal seaport for some of the country's most prosperous farming states, Maryland, Delaware, and Virginia, and she rightly considered herself a headquarters for seafaring men. Her banks were among the wealthiest and most stable in the nation; she was the home of almost as many factories as Philadelphia, Boston, and New York, all of them older cities; and she was proud of her heritage.

That pride was well founded. Her sons had served with distinction in the Revolution, and a younger generation of her sailors and soldiers formed part of the solid, hard core of the Navy and Army. Most of her fighting men were in distant places, and in her hour of greatest trial she had to depend on civilians, who were led, in the main, by officers home on leave of absence.

Thanks to President Madison's prompt warning, the citizens of Baltimore had a precious twenty-four hours to prepare for the massive invasion launched by the Royal Navy and General Ross's Army veterans. A series of forts dotted the waterfront, some of them small wooden structures that housed only one or two cannon. Substantial and built of logs, they were nevertheless cramped, and could accommodate no more than a platoon of soldiers. Naval inspectors made certain that their guns were in good working order, and each was given a quota of powder and cannonballs. Militiamen who were expert marksmen were assigned to duty behind their barricades and were joined there by volunteer civilians, many of them older men who had fought under Washington and Greene in the Revolution.

By far the most important of the defensive works was Fort McHenry, a huge structure of log-reinforced stone. It had been enlarged and strengthened several times since the nation's earliest days, and was armed with more than one hundred cannon. "She's the equal of two ships-of-the-line," said Captain Charles Parker of the Navy, who was in charge of her gun crews. "In fact, she's stronger. Stone can take a blamesight worse pounding than wooden ships."

Only men of experience were accepted for service at Fort McHenry. Luckily, the entire crew of a frigate being built at the government's shipyards was on hand, and all were veterans. Some had seen duty on the *Constitution*, others on the *United States*, a few on the ill-fated *Chesapeake*.

They prepared calmly for battle under the direction of their own officers, placing their cannonballs in neat mounds, carefully protecting their gunpowder behind thick iron shields and making certain they had enough swabs on hand to clean their guns when necessary.

The fate of Baltimore depended in large part on their skill, but the Navy and Army officers who held a council of war in the stone-lined office of the commandant wanted to do still more to protect the city.

Colonel Harvey Brown, a hard-bitten Regular Army officer, puffed silently on his pipe for some minutes, not hearing the talk that swirled around him. Then, suddenly, he raised a hand for silence. "Gentlemen," he said, "I was only an ensign at the time, but I'll never forget something we did during the Revolution when we were afraid the Royal Navy planned to send a fleet up the Hudson. We collected the cable chains of the biggest anchor lines we could find and stretched them across the river at West Point. No ship, large or small, was able to sail past that point."

Captain Parker jumped to his feet. "That's precisely what we need now!" he exclaimed. "If we string several strands of chain across the entrance to the Patapsco, below Fort McHenry, the British fleet will be held at bay while our guns pound ship after ship to bits!"

The idea was enthusiastically approved, but an immediate complication developed. There weren't chains heavy enough and long enough in Baltimore to accomplish the purpose. Huge piles of the links were available in Philadelphia, but at least two or three days would be needed to send a wagon train there, collect the hardware, and return with it. No one dared to hope that the enemy would grant the defenders such a respite, but Baltimore snatched at the remote hope, and thirty wagons, each harnessed to a team of strong horses, were sent off at once.

The British admirals and generals unwittingly played into the hands of the Americans. They were lulled into a false sense of security by the lack of opposition they had encountered in their attack on Washington City. Officers complained that their men were tired after spending long weeks at sea, and everyone was anxious to eat food more palatable than pickled meats and biscuits that had to be soaked in water or wine before they were soft enough for a man to chew them.

The bounty of the American countryside in harvest season was dazzling. So the great warships and huge troop transports rode quietly at anchor in Chesapeake Bay. The admirals and generals knew the Americans were too weak to retaliate. So most of their men rested, enjoyed the sun, and swam, while raiding parties ranged through the Maryland and Virginia countryside. Sides of beef and hams, fresh vegetables, and sacks of grain were seized, and the invaders enjoyed nightly feasts. They were so contemptuous of the Americans that they cooked their meals on shore over great fires, and their sentries found it easy to drive off the few Yankee snipers who tried to disrupt the festivities.

In the meantime, Baltimore improved her defenses. The heavily laden carts returned from Philadelphia. Three links of stout chain were stretched across the main channel of the Patapsco below Fort McHenry, their ends held in place by spikes fashioned of strong, hastily felled trees. Taking no chances, the defenders placed similar barriers across the smaller deep-water channels, too.

Calls for help went out to neighboring states, and their citizens unhesitantly responded to the appeals. From the town of Wilmington, in nearby Delaware, came tons of fine-ground gunpowder made at the nation's largest munitions plant, established there twelve years earlier. Secretary Monroe transferred a full brigade of Regular Army infantry from New Jersey to Baltimore and, more important, moved five batteries of field artillery there from Pennsylvania. Philadelphia sent food to her sister-city so that no one would starve in a siege. And from towns and farms everywhere on the seacoast, from New England to South Carolina, came volunteer marksmen, most of them carrying their own muskets and rifles.

Secretary Monroe, acting with the President's hearty approval, went to Baltimore himself to direct and coordinate the city's preparations. Every hour of respite was precious, and every hour was utilized to the full.

Finally, on September 11, 1814, the British giant stirred, flexed his muscles, and moved. The powerful Royal Navy fleet sailed up Chesapeake Bay in battle formation, sloops of war leading the armada and hovering on the flanks, like dogs shepherding a flock of sheep. Then came the frigates, each of them the equal of the largest and most powerful vessels in the United States Navy. Bomb ketches capable of blowing up warehouses—or forts, if they could edge close enough to their targets—rode close beside the frigates. Bringing up the rear were the great "Seventy-Fours," ships-of-the-line that mounted seventy-four or more cannon, vessels whose fire power was greater than that of any other ships afloat on the seven seas.

Baltimore was ready. Several privateers, all of them merchantmen which had mounted small cannon, had anchored just inside the protective links of chain. Their masters had volunteered for this hazardous duty, well aware they would draw the first fury of enemy fire. These brave men were willing to sacrifice their ships so that gunners in Fort McHenry and the smaller bastions would have more time to pound at the invaders without distraction.

Full crews of experienced gunners manned every cannon. And thanks to Secretary Monroe's energetic leadership, supplies of ammunition and powder were ample for a long battle.

The city had taken care to protect her own flanks, too. Breastworks five feet high had been thrown up in a perimeter that extended in a three-quarter circle around the community, protecting her on all sides except that portion which faced the water. These positions were manned by the most experienced militiamen, bolstered by Regulars. If the Redcoats came ashore and tried to take the city from the rear or sides while the Royal Navy created a diversion in Chesapeake Bay, they would find the defenders prepared. There would be no repetition of the disgraceful panic that had routed the defenders of Washington City.

"Hold your fire," Colonel Brown cautioned, and Captain Parker told the gunners at Fort McHenry to rest easy.

There would be plenty of time for the Yankee cannoneers to prove their marksmanship.

The silence in the moments preceding the opening of the battle was eerie. Then, suddenly, two ships-of-the-line that had swung abreast of the forts greeted Baltimore with a deafening salvo. The British gunners had not yet found their range, but the noise was frightening, even though the cannonballs dropped harmlessly into the water. The steeple of St. Mary's Church, located only a few short blocks from the waterfront, swayed as though the ground had been shaken by a great quake. Gulls rose high into the air above the billowing clouds of smoke, screaming in fear and anger.

The sloops continued to inch forward, to the grim amusement of the defenders watching from concealed positions behind the battlements, and there was a harsh, splintering sound as wood grated against the metal links of the great chains.

Signals rose to the topgallants of the sloops as the news was conveyed to the admirals on board the ships-of-the-line: Baltimore was not as helpless as she appeared.

The Royal Navy reacted to the information promptly, and longboats were launched. It was apparent that the invaders hoped to cut the chains.

Yankee riflemen in the forts had other plans. Continuing to hold their fire until the longboats drew closer, they were finally given the command, "Fire at will!"

Rifles spoke sharply, and the deadly tattoo reverberated across the waterfront. The fire was maintained for more than a quarter of an hour, and at the end of that time at least half of the sailors in the boats were either dead or wounded. The survivors managed to return to the ships, and the chains protecting the approaches to Baltimore remained untouched.

The men in the forts braced themselves. It was obvious to even the youngest recruit that the chains could be removed only if the forts themselves were first destroyed. Therefore the most sensible approach the admirals could take would be to concentrate their cannon fire on Fort McHenry and the smaller bastions.

The ships-of-the-line and frigates went to work almost at once, with a vengeance. The forts replied, and the artillery duel lasted the better part of the afternoon.

In the meantime, Redcoat patrols were landed outside the breastworks, with orders to take military prisoners who could tell the invaders the city's defense plans. Heavy musket and rifle fire drove them away. But one patrol managed to capture an innocent bystander, a Washington City lawyer who was traveling to Baltimore in order to be at the side of his daughter and son-in-law during the city's travail. He was taken out to the fleet but was unable to tell his captors anything of value.

His kidnapping was reported by the militiamen who had witnessed the incident, and soon the whole city was buzzing with the news. One of those most disturbed was Francis Scott Key, a native of Fredericksburg, Maryland, who was a Washington City attorney and a friend of the captured civilian. He went from the home of the friends he was visiting to the American headquarters at Fort McHenry, but the colonels and captains were too busy to see him, and he was advised to return the following day.

By unspoken agreement, both sides halted their bombardment at sundown. The Americans needed a respite to repair some of the smaller forts. And the British were anxious to withdraw several sloops and a frigate that had suffered heavily.

That night the defenders burned bright flares on shore to prevent the enemy from trying to cut the chains of the cables in the dark. Sharpshooters remained at their posts, ready to repel any such invaders, and the British were unable to repeat their costly experiment.

Early the next morning the artillery duel was resumed. Less than an hour later, Francis Scott Key appeared at Fort McHenry to explain his friend's predicament. Captain Parker, his face and clothes powder-stained, his face etched with deep lines of fatigue, made time to listen.

He nodded sympathetically when the lawyer finished his story. "I agree it's unfair for a noncombatant to have been taken prisoner, but I'm not sure what can be done about it at the moment." The steady roar of cannon emphasized his point.

"I'd like to row out to the fleet and arrange for my friend's release," Key said.

"You realize, of course, that you'll be facing a rather great personal risk?"

"I'm willing to take it, sir."

Captain Parker was impressed. "Very well, Mr. Key. I'll see what can be done."

An hour later a white truce flag was raised beside the Stars and Stripes on Fort McHenry. The American guns stopped firing, and a few moments later the British cannon fell silent, too. Key was given a light rowboat, and with the forces of both sides watching, he slowly paddled out to a huge ship-of-the-line that flew the personal pennant of the Admiral commanding the Royal Navy flotilla.

There he found the British in a ferment of activity. Vast quantities of ammunition and powder were being taken on board from supply ships, and it was obvious, even to a civilian, that the invaders intended to keep up their bombardment after dark that night, should it prove necessary. Royal Marines were preparing to go ashore, too, in a storming operation of some sort. Key, waiting to be received, watched them sharpening their bayonets and smearing a film of burned lamp-oil on their uniform buckles and buttons so their insignia wouldn't shine in the dark.

Finally, after a long wait, Key was escorted to the cabin of a Royal Navy captain who was a senior officer on the

Admiral's staff. The lawyer identified himself and explained his mission, sometimes raising his voice to a shout in order to make himself heard above the thunder of the artillery duel, which had been resumed.

The Captain was courteous but firm. "We've been wondering what to do with the gentleman in question, and we'll be delighted to send him ashore with you. But I'm afraid that both of you will have to remain here as—ah—guests of His Majesty's Navy until tomorrow."

Francis Scott Key blinked in surprise.

"You're no fool, sir, and you've seen certain preparations being made by the fleet that your friends ashore would give a great deal to know. I'm afraid we'll have to detain you until our plans have been carried out."

The lawyer was escorted to a section of the main deck where he could not interfere with the busy activities. He walked to the rail and stared at the blazing guns of Fort McHenry and the flag flying from a mast above her parapets. The fate of Baltimore would be decided in the next thirty-six hours, and Key, seeing the mighty armada at close range, knew that the city's peril was far greater than he had realized.

Shots were exchanged all day, and the American gunners proved so accurate that the British resorted to moving their vessels to new positions. This maneuver forced the defenders to change their sights and begin again. Meanwhile the Royal Navy cannoneers were demonstrating that they were far from inept. They knocked out the guns of several small defending bastions and began to concentrate their heaviest blows on Fort McHenry. If they could silence her cannon, it would be relatively simple for British seamen to cut or remove the chains that barred the fleet's entrance to the Patapsco. And once those links were gone, the great Royal Navy ships could sail up the river and threaten the entire city of Baltimore with destruction.

Night came, and the British doubled and redoubled the

fury of their bombardment. Now they fired exploding shells as well as solid iron cannonballs, and guns by the hundred made Fort McHenry their target. Marines and Redcoats went ashore, too, and the sudden flashes of light, the incessant roar of guns made the waterfront an inferno.

Francis Scott Key paced up and down the deck of the British warship in a fever of worry and excitement. This quiet lawyer in his mid-thirties knew virtually nothing of war, but couldn't imagine how the defenders could hold out under such relentless pressure. His worst nightmares were coming true.

If Baltimore fell, both Philadelphia and New York would be threatened, too. The New England secessionists would become alarmed, and President Madison might be forced to sue for peace on humiliating terms. The very existence of the United States as an independent nation was in jeopardy.

The hours passed slowly. Often the clocks in Fort McHenry seemed to stand still. On the deck of the enemy warship, Francis Scott Key thought morning would never come. Huge clouds of black, acrid smoke billowed up, obscuring the land from sight. The thunder of guns deafened him. The throb of explosions numbed him.

Dawn came at last, and the lawyer moved to the rail of the warship. Had Fort McHenry struck her colors? He peered anxiously toward the shore, trying to see through the smoke and early morning haze.

Miraculously, the American flag still flew from her mast above the fort!

Tears of relief filled Key's eyes. Brushing them aside, he felt a wave of patriotic inspiration. He, an attorney who had never written a line of poetry in his life, was so moved that his fingers flew as he scribbled on the back of a legal document he had been carrying in his pocket, the only paper at hand. The words came to him in a rush:

Oh, say can you see, by the dawn's early light,
What so proudly we hailed at the twilight's last gleam-
   ing?
Whose broad stripes and bright stars, thro' the perilous
   fight,
O'er the ramparts we watched were so gallantly stream-
   ing?
And the rockets' red glare, the bombs bursting in air,
Gave proof thro' the night that our flag was still there.
Oh, say does that star-spangled banner yet wave
O'er the land of the free and the home of the brave?

On the shore dimly seen through the mist of the deep,
Where the foe's haughty host in dread silence reposes,
What is that which the breeze, o'er the towering steep,
As it fitfully blows, half conceals, half discloses?
Now it catches the gleam of the morning's first beam,
In full glory reflected, now shines on the stream;
'Tis the star-spangled banner! Oh, long may it wave
O'er the land of the free and the home of the brave!

Oh, thus be it ever, when free men shall stand
Between their loved homes and war's desolation,
Blessed with vict'ry and peace, may the heav'n rescued
   land
Praise the pow'r that hath made and preserved us a
   nation.
Then conquer we must, when our cause it is just,
And this be our motto, "In God is our trust!"
And the star-spangled banner in triumph shall wave
O'er the land of the free and the home of the brave!

Francis Scott Key had no idea, when he went ashore that
morning with his friend, his mission completed, that his
poem would soon take the country by storm. Friends would

sing it to an old English folk tune that had been popular for more than a half-century. Eventually it would be adopted by both the Army and Navy. And finally, more than a century later, in 1931, Congress would pass a bill making *The Star-Spangled Banner* the National Anthem of the United States.

On the morning of September 13, 1814, Key—like everyone else in Baltimore—could think only in terms of the immediate, wonderful present. The British sea attack had failed. The Royal Marines and Redcoats who had gone ashore had been repulsed.

The great British armada was forced to withdraw, battered but still proud. And Baltimore was still safe.

The British failure at Baltimore made both sides realize that the costly war could drag on for years. Although the fighting continued, with the British still planning their major invasion from the West Indies, responsible men in both Washington City and London knew that the time had come to begin peace negotiations. The United States wanted to devote her growing strength to the development of her great cities and fruitful farms, to an expansion into the vast wilderness territories she had acquired. Great Britain, exhausted after her long war with Napoleon, urgently needed to devote her attention to domestic affairs, too.

Both nations sent commissioners to Ghent, Belgium, for discussions. President Madison was scrupulously fair, as always. Two men acted as co-chairmen of the American delegation. One was War Hawk Henry Clay of Kentucky, representing the West. The other was John Quincy Adams of Massachusetts, one of the most respected of New Englanders.

The President and Secretary Monroe wanted a treaty

that the entire united nation could approve whole-heart-edly.

But, even as the commissioners talked and bargained and argued in Ghent, General Sir Edward Pakenham and a corps of British veterans fifteen thousand strong set sail from Jamaica. America's ordeal was not yet ended.

CHAPTER THIRTEEN

No one knew whether Mobile, New Orleans, or some other
place on the Gulf of Mexico would be the object of a British
raid. But it was apparent to General Andrew Jackson that
a landing would be made somewhere, and he was taking
no chances. He posted strong detachments of troops at
forts facing the Gulf and asked Washington City for reinforcements.

Only a few regiments of Regulars were available, but
Secretary Monroe sent them to him. Additional battalions
of militiamen were mobilized in Kentucky, Tennessee, and
Louisiana, and the General drew on the militia of the Mississippi and Alabama Territories, too. Few of these lean
frontiersmen wore uniforms and fewer still knew how to
salute. But they were incomparable marksmen, and Andrew Jackson was satisfied. He understood his men and they
knew him. He and they, together, were products of the
wilderness.

In mid-December, while the General was visiting New
Orleans on an inspection trip, word was received that a
large British force had landed one hundred miles away, in
the delta country of the Mississippi River, and had captured
five American gunboats. Hysterical panic threatened to
overwhelm the city. General Jackson, acting on his own
authority, proclaimed martial law and began to round up
his fighting men, who were scattered all over the South.

Brigades of infantry sharpshooters from Tennessee, Kentucky, and the Mississippi Territory were the first to join him, and New Orleans breathed easier. Spirits rose still higher on December 20th when John Coffee, now a brigadier general, rode into the city at the head of a column of one thousand cavalrymen. The following day a flotilla of barges carrying General William Carroll's division of Tennesseeans swept down the Mississippi. Three regiments of Regulars came in on December 22nd, as did two of hard-riding Mississippi Dragoons. The Louisiana militiamen originally posted in the city had been sent off to block the approaches from the delta. And Jackson wrote to Monroe, saying the enemy would be repulsed far to the south.

But the enemy upset his careful calculations by slipping past his inexperienced militiamen. At two o'clock on the afternoon of January 23rd, Major Gabriel Villeré, son of the Louisiana militia commander, arrived at Jackson's headquarters in New Orleans with an incredible story.

The vanguard of a British force estimated at fifteen to twenty thousand veterans had arrived at his plantation, only eight miles from the center of the city. They had captured him, but he had managed to escape and carry the alarm to the waiting corps.

Andrew Jackson had been taking a nap on a sofa in the room he used as an office. He jumped to his feet, crashed a fist on his desk, and shouted, "By the Eternal, the enemy shall not sleep on our soil!" Then he became calmer, summoned his staff, and said quietly, "Gentlemen, the British are below. We will fight them tonight."

Orders were issued at once, and the five thousand defenders marched south, moving very quietly, and halted at the bank of a canal near Villeré's plantation. Although outnumbered at least three to one, General Jackson decided that a surprise attack would be his best defense. When the gunboat *Carolina* sailed down the Mississippi from New Orleans to give him much-needed artillery support, he was ready to act.

At seven-thirty in the evening the *Carolina* opened a steady fire on the British, bombarding them for a half-hour. General Pakenham, unaware that American troops were nearby, concentrated his return fire on the gunboat.

Promptly at eight o'clock John Coffee's horsemen rode out across the fields of sugar-cane stubble, closely followed by two regiments of Regulars and three of militia. Rifle and musket fire caught the enemy unaware, and the Battle of New Orleans was joined.

British casualties were heavy, but Pakenham's veterans rallied swiftly, and the fight raged until midnight. At the very least, the British timetable of reinforcing its vanguard was completely upset. And Andrew Jackson had served notice on the foe that they could advance no farther.

But the battle had just begun, and couriers arrived at the headquarters in the city throughout the night with an unending series of requests from the determined Jackson. He demanded fighting men, weapons, and, above all, spades and shovels. By dawn the entire corps was at work, digging into the rich Louisiana soil and throwing up a breastworks. The line stretched from the Mississippi River on one side, across open fields of sugar-cane stubble, to a deep patch of thick woods, where militiamen at home in the forests were stationed.

Men toiled ceaselessly throughout the day and all night on Christmas Eve, deepening the ditch and raising the breastworks higher. The work was so tiring that the companies of each battalion labored in shifts, one digging while another slept on its rifles.

General Jackson neither slept nor rested. He rode incessantly up and down his line, inspecting, encouraging the weary, and sending aides off to the city for still more tools, still more help. He was suffering from a stomach ailment

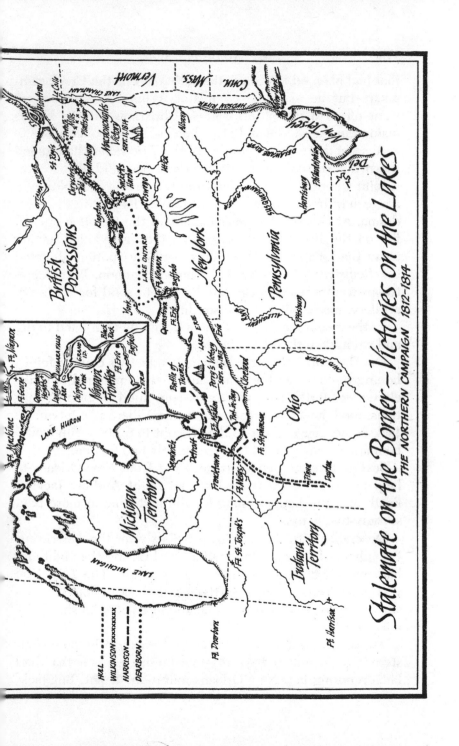

Stalemate on the Border—Victories on the Lakes
THE NORTHERN CAMPAIGN 1812-1814

that had plagued him since the early days of the Creek campaign, but he made no complaint. When his staff officers went off to a campfire for their Christmas dinner, he remained in the saddle and ate a bowl of plain boiled rice.

A second American gunboat, the *Louisiana,* had sailed down the Mississippi to join the defenders and anchored at a point where it was shielded from the enemy by a bluff and a screen of trees. There it waited to play its part in the great drama. At General Jackson's command the *Carolina* opened fire on the British, and as soon as they responded, giving away the location of their guns, artillery spotters directed the *Louisiana's* fire toward the enemy cannon. Pakenham's troops were pinned down, and he had to send for his heavy artillery, many miles to the south.

In the meantime, Jackson's men doggedly continued to dig and strengthen their breastworks.

On December 26th, Pakenham made two clumsy feints, hoping to convince the Americans that he planned to strike elsewhere. But his supply trains continued to bring munitions, food, and reinforcements to the Villeré plantation. So Jackson became convinced the attempt to destroy him would be made on the ground that he himself had chosen.

Several thousand civilians came out from New Orleans to help prepare the breastworks. That night Andrew Jackson finally went to bed, sleeping for the first time in more than seventy-two hours.

December 27th dawned inauspiciously for the Americans. Pakenham's heavy artillery had arrived during the night and had opened a steady fire on the gunboats. The *Louisiana* was moved out of range in time, but the *Carolina* was destroyed by expert British gunners who cut her to shreds by mid-morning.

The main American defense line was ready now, bolstered by several old twenty-four-pound cannon that had been reposing in a New Orleans munitions depot. But Jackson was still dissatisfied. Wanting to be prepared for any eventuality, he ordered work begun on a second line of breastworks, two miles to the rear.

Late in the afternoon of December 27th, Pakenham launched his first serious infantry attack. The weakest spot in the American line was on the left flank, where the breastworks were only waist-high and the ditch shallow enough for men to cross with relative ease. Waves of scarlet and white rolled forward across the cane fields, and Jackson, watching through his binoculars, knew that Billy Carroll's Tennesseeans were in for trouble.

John Coffee realized it, too, and brought up his cavalry to bolster the flank. General Jackson galloped to the position, once again ignoring personal danger. He estimated that the British were sending at least six thousand men against approximately one thousand mustered by Carroll and Coffee. There was only one immediate solution, and he ordered both the *Louisiana* and the land-based artillery to lay down a barrage in front of the flank.

The gunners immediately opened a heavy fire, forcing the Redcoats to halt, then retire and regroup. Jackson was playing a deadly game of chess with Pakenham, and when he realized that the British commander intended to continue concentrating on the same sector, he reacted accordingly. Two regiments of Regulars were transferred to the flank thereby temporarily weakening the center.

The attack was halted, but Andrew Jackson was acutely aware of the risks he was taking when he allowed one part of his line to deteriorate in order to strengthen another. "I want every arsenal and militia assembly depot within one hundred miles of New Orleans searched for cannon," he told his staff. "I need artillery, and—by the Eternal—I shall have it!"

Scores of men scoured the towns of the hinterland. To the surprise of everyone but the General, they found numerous guns. Some were French, some Spanish, and some American, reflecting Louisiana's changes in allegiance over the period of a few years. All were useful, and within the next two days they were hauled into place behind the left flank. Now the entire American line was secure.

On New Year's Day the British opened fire with a tremendous artillery barrage, obviously hoping to follow it with a cavalry-infantry charge. But the American gunners doggedly answered round for round, and neither side was able to gain an advantage. The net result was that the barricades of both forces were damaged.

Jackson patiently ordered the breastworks repaired, and his scouts told him the British were doing the same. There were several skirmishes in the woods on the right, but the Americans repulsed their enemies without too much difficulty. Meanwhile the Yankee gunners, constantly improving their aim, gave the British no rest.

"I wouldn't be surprised," Jackson said at a meeting with his subordinate generals, "if the Lobsters shift their major attack to some other quarter."

On January 4th a division of twenty-four-hundred Kentucky riflemen floated down the river, cheering the weary citizens of New Orleans and providing General Jackson with badly needed reinforcements. "Now we can hold our own, I reckon," said the gaunt commander-in-chief, whose troops were beginning to call him Old Hickory.

The British soon learned about the presence of the new arrivals, and Jackson's spies brought him word that Pakenham was becoming nervous and irritable. It wasn't difficult to fathom his state of mind: the Americans were fighting on home territory and could call on still more reserves, but he was thousands of miles from England and couldn't increase his corps by a single man. If he hoped to win a decisive victory, he would have to launch an all-out offensive in the fairly immediate future.

The Americans soon gleaned that their foes were making preparations for a major attack. But its objective remained a mystery. Cavalry patrols, acting on General Jackson's instructions, brought in a number of prisoners. The General questioned the captives himself, but they insisted that Pakenham had no intention of shifting to another salient.

They were wrong. Sir Edward kept his plans to himself until the last possible moment and then resorted to daring tactics. Early in the morning of January 8th, General Jackson learned that large numbers of British infantry were crossing the Mississippi to the western bank, where a small unit of only six hundred Louisiana militiamen, bolstered by a few companies of Kentuckians, held a little fort.

The Americans were in danger of being outflanked and of having their entire line turned. But they didn't dare weaken their basic positions. Old Hickory sent word across the river that the Louisiana contingent must hold out at all costs.

The British attack began a short time before dawn. It was launched simultaneously against the left flank, held by Carroll and Coffee, with the bulk of the Kentuckians in reserve, and against the little fort on the far side of the river. Pakenham was relying on cleverness rather than brute strength and used no artillery preparation. The assault was being made solely by infantrymen, who had bayonets attached to their muskets. They were relying on darkness and fog to bring them near to the American lines before they opened fire.

They came close, but not quite close enough, before they were detected. Jackson himself gave the order for his artillery to lay down a barrage. The guns roared. Frontiersmen stationed behind the breastworks resisted the temptation to shoot blindly into the massed ranks of the British. Instead they followed the command of John Coffee, and each soldier carefully chose an individual target.

Three times the Redcoats swept forward, and it seemed

that no force on earth could resist them. But the American lines held steady, and three times the solid ranks halted, were thinned, and retreated. Members of the British high command tried in vain to rally their troops, and Pakenham himself took so many personal risks that he suffered three wounds. The last of them was fatal, and he died on the field, making it impossible for subordinates to conceal the blow from their men.

The British lost the will to fight after they lost Pakenham, and the attack ended as suddenly as it had begun. British dead and wounded littered the field. But the Americans, almost miraculously, had suffered virtually no casualties in this climactic stage of the long battle. General Jackson could scarcely believe the report he received that only six of his men had been killed and even fewer wounded.

In mid-afternoon the American artillery was ordered to cease firing. Some of the Americans rejoiced—prematurely. The battle was not yet ended. The men in the fort on the western bank of the Mississippi were having an extremely difficult time holding out against a force three times their size. Old Hickory sent four hundred infantry to reinforce them, and the gunners, called back to duty, poured a heavy rain of fire on the Redcoats across the river.

Hasty arrangements were set in motion to send still larger bodies of Americans across the Mississippi. But the British commander there was ordered to retire with his troops. His superiors feared, with good cause, that he might be cut off. And when dawn broke, on January 9th, not one cannon, rifle, or musket was fired by either side. The citizens of New Orleans, who had become accustomed to the incessant roar, scarcely dared to hope that the battle had come to a favorable end.

But the incredible, the impossible, the fantastic had indeed occurred. Andrew Jackson, the Nashville lawyer and amateur soldier, had outsmarted the world's finest professional military men. A ragged corps of Regulars, militiamen, and oddly assorted volunteers had won a decisive victory over the superb troops who had beaten the supposedly invincible Napoleon Bonaparte.

Several American officers wanted to send John Coffee's cavalry in pursuit of the retreating foe, but Jackson refused. "The Redcoats will have to withdraw and evacuate the country now," he said. "They no longer have a clear-cut choice. So why risk more lives?"

His prediction proved correct. The British limped painfully down the Mississippi delta to the Gulf of Mexico. And on January 18th the battered remnant of the once-proud expedition set sail from Louisiana. Jackson, gallant to the very last, sent to Major General Keane, the new British commander, the personal sword he had lost on the battlefield.

Keane paid his foes the highest of compliments in the long report he wrote to the War Office in London. "Some of our foes," he said, "may have been amateurs when we first met them. But I have never encountered troops who learned the art of war so rapidly. The Americans are inspired fighting men when ably led and defending their own soil."

On January 21st, the victorious corps, eight thousand strong, marched into New Orleans. The city went wild, flowers were strewn in General Jackson's path, and officials made long speeches, calling Jackson a worthy successor to George Washington.

But the hero of the Battle of New Orleans cut them short. "That's rubbish," he said modestly. "Give the credit to my boys!"

Huge bonfires were lighted in every American city and town when the nation learned of Andrew Jackson's victory. A few days later they celebrated again, when a sloop from Belgium landed at Baltimore, and President Madison received dispatches from Henry Clay and John Quincy Adams to the effect that a peace treaty had been signed at Ghent. The War of 1812 was at an end.

Some government officials were struck by the irony of the situation. "The Battle of New Orleans," they declared, "needn't have taken place. The treaty had actually been signed when Jackson and Pakenham met!"

The far-sighted Secretary Monroe saw the recent events in a different light. "The Battle of New Orleans wasn't fought in vain," he said. "By proving they could fight and win, Andy Jackson's men helped the whole country recover its pride. And for the first time in our history, we've won respect abroad. Foreign powers will think very carefully now before they dare to abuse or attack the United States of America."

CHAPTER FOURTEEN

The United States reaped a rich harvest from the War of 1812. Perhaps the most obvious result was that a new generation of exceptionally able men took command of the nation's destiny and guided her affairs for more than a quarter of a century.

The quietly competent James Monroe succeeded Madison as President of the United States, taking office on March 4, 1817. Sectional differences had been forgotten, the old Federalist party had withered away, and the nation had been truly united. Men in New England and the Middle Atlantic states, in the South and in the West, thought of themselves first and foremost as Americans. There were no political parties active in the country during the eight years of Monroe's administration, and the period became known as the Era of Good Feeling.

John Quincy Adams of Massachusetts was elected to succeed Monroe in the White House. This able executive, son of President John Adams, had an astounding, unique career. After serving as President, he spent many years in the House of Representatives, where he acted as the conscience of America.

Andrew Jackson won his reward. His popularity soared to even greater heights after he conducted a brief campaign in Florida and made it possible for the United States to acquire that territory from Spain. He followed John Quincy

Adams as President, and during his eight years in office Jacksonian democracy flowered. The "common man"—the ordinary citizen—gained a voice in the affairs of government which the people have never relinquished.

William Henry Harrison eventually won the high honor of being elected President, too. But his term was marred by tragedy: he died after spending only one month in office.

The "great triumvirate"—Henry Clay, Daniel Webster, and John C. Calhoun—served their country with great distinction for many years. All were leaders in the Senate, all held Cabinet posts of great responsibility at one time or another, and Calhoun was also Vice President.

The United States Navy at last came into her own as a great sea power, a position she has never relinquished. Under the leadership of Commodores Hull and Bainbridge, Decatur and Perry, a large and efficient fleet was established and maintained, making American merchant ships safe everywhere on the earth's seven seas.

The United States Army became a strong, proud fighting force. General Winfield Scott became its commander, a position he held until his retirement at the eve of the Civil War, and it was he who led American troops to victory in the Mexican War.

It was the people of America who enjoyed the greatest benefits of the War of 1812. Captain David Shoemaker, the courageous young militia officer who had tried in vain to rally his troops during the British attack on Washington City, was typical of the fortunate many.

He married his childhood sweetheart, and they moved to the rapidly growing town of Pittsburgh, Pennsylvania. There, in a region where coal was abundant, and broad, swift-flowing rivers solved problems of transportation, he established his own iron foundry. He worked hard, and in the 1830's was

able to look back over the years and make a sober estimate
of all that had happened to him—and to the country.

"Mary," he said to his wife as they sat at the dinner table
with their four children, "it's hard to believe. When my
militiamen scattered on the approaches to Washington City,
I thought it was the end of the world that we knew and
loved. In a sense it was. I never dreamed, that day, that we'd
become a great and powerful country. My foundry is successful—and there are thousands of other industrial plants
that have sprung up everywhere, from the Atlantic seaboard
to the Mississippi. We're becoming stronger and more prosperous with each passing year. We have as many factories as
farms—and we're still growing."

"You aren't the only one who feels that way." Mrs. Shoemaker smiled as she unfolded a letter they had received just
that morning from their eldest son, David, Jr. "'You stay-at-
homes don't know what you're missing,'" she read. "'Life
here in Chicago is wonderful. Ten new factories have opened
in the past month, and so many immigrants are coming here
from Europe that we can't build houses fast enough for them.
And the languages we hear! German and Italian and Polish
and Bohemian. I tell you, Chicago is going to be one of the
biggest cities in the world!'"

The younger children giggled, remembering that when
their brother had gone to the new town at the southern end
of Lake Michigan only a few years earlier it had consisted
of a collection of mud huts.

"Don't laugh," Shoemaker told them. "Your brother is
probably right. There's no reason why Chicago shouldn't become a great city. I imagine there will be others, still farther
west. You see, we didn't know it at the time, but the War of
1812 did this country a favor. We had to depend on our own
manufactured goods, so we started building our own factories and plants. We've scarcely begun, and I don't believe

we'll ever stop. The United States has almost unlimited re-
sources."

Mrs. Shoemaker passed the platters heaped high with vegetables.

Her husband stood to carve the smoking, juicy roast of
beef. "Why," he asked the children, "do you suppose that
people are crossing the Atlantic by the hundreds of thousands to make their homes here?"

Twelve-year-old Tommy frowned and thought for a moment. "It's because we have so much land."

"That's part of the reason," his father replied. "There's
enough land for all who want to be farmers, enough oppor-
tunity for all who want to live in the cities. But there's something far more important. We proved to Europe in the War
of 1812 that we love freedom more than life itself. We risked
everything for the sake of liberty. We've become a symbol
of freedom to the whole world, and that's why men are
migrating here. They want to enjoy liberty and its benefits,
too."

Life at Saginaw had become too tame for Andy Merriwether. Michigan would soon be granted statehood, Detroit
had become a great city, and Indians of every tribe had vanished from the area. A widower in the mid-1830's, Andy
called his two young sons to what he called a "council of
war."

"Boys," he said, "we have a comfortable home here. The
produce from the farm and the fish in Lake Huron give
us a fair enough living. But I'm bored. Others are having all
the fun, all the excitement, and we're missing it. You've never
gone trapping. Some of our newer neighbors think I'm odd
because I've taught you to shoot rifles, but even the woods
here have become so domesticated that you won't find game
in them."

His fifteen-year-old son, named after William Henry Harrison, leaned forward on the homemade bench opposite his father and grinned. "What do you have on your mind, Pa?"

"I've got a hankering to go out to the Iowa Territory," Andy replied. "The western part, on the Missouri River. I hear tell it's really wild country. There are buffalo on the plains, beaver by the thousand on the Missouri and the smaller rivers. And I've been told the soil is richer and blacker that anywhere else in the world. I'd like to sell this place and move out there."

Both boys cheered.

Their father held up a restraining hand. "Hold on, now," he cautioned. "Frontier living isn't easy, and anybody who thinks it is will wake up with some rude shocks. We'll have to stake out our claim, clear our land, and cut the trees to make our cabin. There are bears in the forests and bobcats in the hills. And the savages are still more dangerous. The Sioux have settled out there, and there isn't a tribe in all North America as ready to scalp a settler and cut out his heart."

Willie Merriwether was still grinning. "Suppose we don't go, Pa? Then what happens?"

"Oh, we could stay here at home, of course. But other men will take our places on the march west, I can tell you that. Nothing can stop the expansion of the United States. The frontier is in our blood."

The boy solemnly extended his hand. "I'm ready to leave whenever you say the word, Pa. That's the life for me."

Andy Merriwether laughed proudly as he clasped his son's hand. "Spoken like a real American!"

The U.S.S. *James Madison,* her sails billowing, left scarcely a ripple in her wake as she cut through the waters of the eastern Atlantic. Captain Joseph Bainbridge, nephew of the late, great Commodore, stood on his quarterdeck and thought that his ship behaved as she should. The newest frigate in

American service was worthy of her name and of the service she represented.

Fanning out ahead were four agile sloops, to the *Madison's* port was the *Constellation*, and holding the place of honor to starboard was the *Constitution*. This was no ordinary sea exercise, and Captain Joseph Bainbridge smiled as he saw the pennant flying from the *Constitution's* topgallants. It was the personal ensign of Commodore Isaac Hull, her first captain and now the senior officer on active duty in the Navy.

At the personal orders of President Jackson, Commodore Hull was traveling to the great capitals of Europe, London and Paris and Madrid, Copenhagen and Stockholm and Moscow, on a farewell tour before his retirement. Jackson, always so modest about his own accomplishments, wanted Hull to have a final taste of glory before taking off his blue and gold uniform for the last time.

The *Constitution* hoisted multi-colored bits of cloth, and a signal lieutenant materialized at his captain's side to interpret them. "Unidentified squadron approaching off the port bow, sir."

The major nations of the world were at peace, so the *Madison's* gunports remained closed. Her crew, young sailors from all twenty-four states of the growing Union and from the Arkansas Territory, soon to be admitted as the twenty-fifth, were calm and curious as they watched the strangers drawing closer.

The Captain felt his throat become dry and his muscles grow taut when he recognized a powerful squadron of the British Navy. There were two mammoth ships-of-the-line in the center, each of them powerful enough to blow virtually any other vessel afloat out of the water. There were several frigates, too, and a large number of sloops and other smaller craft.

William Bainbridge's nephew had been a cabin boy on

board the *Constitution* when his uncle had sunk the *Java*. And even now, more than twenty years after that grim, exciting day, he couldn't help becoming tense when he saw warships of the Royal Navy.

But the British quickly revealed their intentions. The flagship raised the Union Jack, and the *Constitution* responded by hoisting the Stars and Stripes. The squadron drew still closer. Suddenly, massed bugle and drum corps on the decks of the two ships-of-the-line began to play *The Star-Spangled Banner*.

Captain Joseph Bainbridge stood at attention and raised his right hand to the brim of his gold-braided hat. Great Britain, once America's deadly foe, was saluting Commodore Hull and the Navy he represented and, above all, honoring the United States of America.

The British squadron tacked, came about and, in an unprecedented maneuver, led the American warships as they sailed toward England. Old hatreds were forgotten, and men lined the decks of both fleets to cheer.

The Captain trained his glass on Commodore Hull, who was standing erect on the quarterdeck of the *Constitution,* and saw there were tears in his eyes. The nation for which he had fought so valiantly was being recognized as a great land, a free land, an independent land by her former enemies.

Bugles blared, drums throbbed, and the Captain knew, more certainly than ever before, that Mr. Madison's War had not been fought in vain.

Bibliography

Adams, Henry. *History of the United States During the Administrations of Jefferson and Madison*, 4 vols., New York, A. & C. Boni, 1930.

Brant, Irving. *James Madison*, vols. 5 & 6, Indianapolis, Bobbs-Merrill, 1961.

Carr, Albert H. Z. *The Coming of War*, New York, Doubleday, 1960.

Cleeves, Freeman. *Old Tippecanoe: William Henry Harrison*, New York, Scribner's, 1939.

James, Marquis. *Andrew Jackson: Portrait of a President*, New York, Garden City Publishing Co., 1937.

Koch, Adrienne. *Jefferson and Madison: The Great Collaboration*, New York, Knopf, 1950.

Lewis, A. E. *The War of 1812: a Military History*, New York, Harper, 1949.

Mahan, A. T. *Sea Power in its Relations to the War of 1812*, 2 vols., Boston, Little, Brown & Co., 1905.

Morgan, George. *The Life of James Monroe*, Boston, Small, Maynard and Co., 1921.

Pratt, Julius W. *Expansionists of 1812*, New York, The Macmillan Co., 1925.

Updyke, Frank A. *Diplomacy of the War of 1812*, Baltimore, The Johns Hopkins Press, 1915.

Van Doren, Carl. *The Great Rehearsal*, New York, Viking Press, 1948.

Index

About the Author

NOEL B. GERSON is the author of many books, both fiction and non-fiction, for adults and young people. Born in Chicago, Illinois, on November 6, 1914, he is a graduate of the University of Chicago. A former newspaperman and foreign correspondent, he has also written many radio and television plays, documentaries, magazine articles and short stories. Mr. Gerson and his family live in Waterford, Connecticut. When not glued to his typewriter, he enjoys swimming and gardening.